FULL COLOR

Planner for A Magical

2025

AMY CESARI

Be a fire-safe witch!

Lots of space above
and around the flame.

Candle is on a
fire-safe dish.

Never leave
flames unattended.

COPYRIGHT & GENERAL DISCLAIMER:

COLORING BOOK OF SHADOWS: PLANNER FOR A MAGICAL 2025
ALL TEXT AND IMAGES © 2024 BOOK OF SHADOWS LLC, AMY CESARI

This Book Belongs To:

I Solemnly Swear
That I'll Make the Most of this Magical Year

Pull tarot cards, cast rune stones, or write your own words of wisdom for each month of the year. Contemplate them at the beginning of the year or do it month-by month as a "look ahead" or a reflection of what's passed.

JANUARY
OWL
Where is the magic in your shadow?

FEBRUARY
CAT
How can you balance curiosity and comfort?

MARCH
RABBIT
What sparks you to take action?

APRIL
RAT
What reminds you that you are capable?

MAY
GOAT
How do you unlock your power and strength?

JUNE
TOAD
How can you feel magic in a mundane world?

MAGIC?! IT'S ALREADY WITHIN YOU.

The most widely accepted definition of magic is the ability to influence your destiny. Magic is aligning your intention, will, and the natural forces around you—such as the moon, the sun, the planets, the Earth, and the changing seasons.

But "animal magic" is even simpler than that. Animals teach us about ourselves and help us to feel present and whole just as we are. They are a mirror to our wild roots, our true nature, and our inner power. Have you always felt a connection to animals? Have you ever wished you were an animal in the wild? Or have you seen an animal and wondered what message it had for you?

Animal magic is all of these things, but it's also about accepting ourselves just as we are. Animals show us that we have power, presence, and potential—right now.

As humans, we often find ourselves stuck between the limits of the past and fear of the future. And we can escape this stuckness by feeling the presence of animal archetypes.

Animals live in the present moment. You can't change the past, but you can influence your future by how you show up right now, in the present. When you live as your empowered, authentic, "animal" self, you create the future from wholeness, not lack.

Do this consistently and you will make magic happen. You've already got this power within you. It's yours! You're ready! So... let's try it...

CONNECTING TO ANIMAL ARCHETYPES

1. Close your eyes and imagine that you are an animal. Pick the first one that comes.

2. Pause for a moment and just observe. From outside of yourself—from the animal's perspective—see yourself as whole and complete in the present moment. (Then notice... where did all of your human worries, fears, and stories go? Set them aside... for now.)

4. Then feel your intention for the future that you wish to create. What do you want?

5. Ask the animal if it has any wisdom to share with you—what is the animal's message?

When you see yourself through the persona of an animal, you'll shift your energy and free your spirit to be present. You'll feel a little bit more magical, capable, and clear.

The magic of animals will reconnect you to your own inner guidance and intuition—because after all, we are animals, too.

So... are you ready for a year of magic?! (Say "yes!"). *Excellent.* Here we go.

TIPS TO USE THIS PLANNER

1. Familiarize yourself with the introduction and basics of magic and spellcasting.
2. Fill out the "MAGICAL VISION" planning pages at the end of the introduction.
3. Try to perform the "big spell" or one of the mini-spells in this book each month.
4. Review your MAGICAL VISION monthly, whenever you like, or on the new moons. Adjust as needed. Break your goals into smaller intentions and actions for each month, and take small, purposeful actions forward if desired, step by step.
5. Repeat this process for as many of the 12 months of the year as you can to "stir the cauldron" and see what happens... (...will magic happen?! Let's hope so!)

GOALS, PLANS, AND INTENTIONS

Yes, this is a planner, but that doesn't mean you have to get intense about... planning. You can even plan to do less this year. In fact, that's a great idea. Get to know what *you* want (not your family, not society, etc...) and then use the powers of magic and intention to focus your energy on those things. Here are some tips:

• Less is more. Go for broader feelings and intentions rather than super specific dates, processes, and outcomes. Leave room for magic to surprise you in fantastic ways.

• Make your goals as big or small as you want.

• Instead of saying what you don't want, "to stop being an emotional wreck," phrase it positively so you feel good when you say it, "to feel at ease with all of my emotions."

• Any plans you make are more of a guideline. Don't be afraid to scrap them and do something else if they don't feel right anymore. It's never too late to change directions or make new plans—in fact, that's often where the real magic comes into play.

ABOUT THIS BOOK

• Write, & color in this book! Expressing your thoughts in writing is a powerful way to create your reality. Here are some ideas: *Your day-to-day-mundane appointments. Daily gratitude. Daily reflections. Daily tarot. A diary of your spiritual journey. Intuitive messages. How you feel during different moon phases.*

• "Spellcasting Basics" are included if you're brand-new to magic. Please read this if so.

• And remember, the magic is inside you. Even if you start this book "late" or if it's not "the best" moon phase for a spell, you are the real power behind your magical life.

HOW TO USE ANIMAL MAGIC

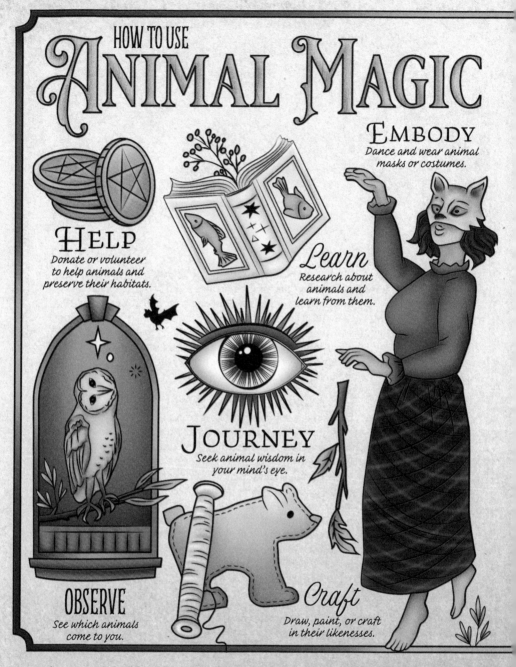

EMBODY
Dance and wear animal masks or costumes.

HELP
Donate or volunteer to help animals and preserve their habitats.

Learn
Research about animals and learn from them.

JOURNEY
Seek animal wisdom in your mind's eye.

OBSERVE
See which animals come to you.

Craft
Draw, paint, or craft in their likenesses.

How do you use animal magic? You can feel it and use it simply by witnessing the energy and wisdom that animals embody.

The animals you encounter in daily life—a scampering squirrel, a buzzing bee, or a cozy cat—are not mere coincidences. They are whispers of magic and intuition, reminding you of your connection to your inner wisdom and the powers of natural magic that are all around you.

When you notice animals, they are showing you subconscious signs that you are on the right path. Your inner guidance is as true for you as it is for animals, and you can trust your senses.

Every animal has a unique magic and wisdom. You may want to experience animal magic by observing animals, either by seeking them out or waiting to see which animals make themselves known to you. You might like to "journey" to meet animals in your mind's eye or notice which animals appear in your dreams. Perhaps you

Notice
Take note if animals
visit you in dreams.

REFLECT
Work with animal
oracle cards.

Decorate
Place symbols on
your altar.

GROW Make your garden a
wildlife sanctuary.

SYMBOLIZE
Use magical tools with
animal motifs and symbols.

Find bones or
feathers.

VISIT
Seek out animals in
their natural habitats.

Be
... and sometimes animals simply
help us to feel like we are not alone.

prefer to place animal figures on your altar or wear masks or clothing with animal symbolism. Anytime you see, feel, or think about an animal is an opportunity to work with animal magic.

What matters most is the feeling and way of being that animals evoke in you. When you connect to the energy of animals and their ways of being—their innate magic— you will connect to the innate magic within yourself.

Animal archetypes speak specifically to you in each encounter. There is no book that can give you all the answers. Ask the animal for its message, then go within and interpret it through your own lens of what you are seeking.

So... set an intention to embrace the magic of animals and nature this year. Be present, and open yourself to the signs of the natural world around you. You'll find that you'll discover the full spectrum of your magical potential in a way that is natural, powerful, and meaningful to you.

ANIMAL SYMBOLS &

SNAKES
symbolize transformation, occult wisdom, and releasing the past.

Birds
represent spirit, life, and freedom. Many believe that birds can embody the spirits of deceased loved ones.

CATS
symbolize magic and the wisdom that comes from knowing yourself.

ANIMALS WITH HOOVES & horns
teach us about power, strength, and tenacity.

Fish
represent flowing with changing tides.

DOGS & WOLVES
symbolize loyalty, family, and self-acceptance.

MAGICAL CREATURES

Not a complete list.
Add your own!

"GIANTS"
like rhinos, elephants, and
whales symbolize personal
power and sovereignty.

OWLS & BATS
represent mysteries and
secrets of the dark.

Butterflies
Immortality of spirit.

Bees
Productivity
& nature's sweetness.

FROGS & TOADS
symbolize magic and transformation.

RACCOONS
& WOODLAND CREATURES
remind us to live authentically
and seek out simple pleasures.

Rats & Mice
remind us that we are capable and clever.

RABBITS
embody the polarity of
stillness and action.

YOUR ANIMAL MAGIC

Animal magic is unique to you, where you live, and what you experience. Write down which animals you see this year and what they mean to you.

- Giraffe -
Foreseeing the future

- Otter -
Playfulness

- Rooster -
Enthusiasm

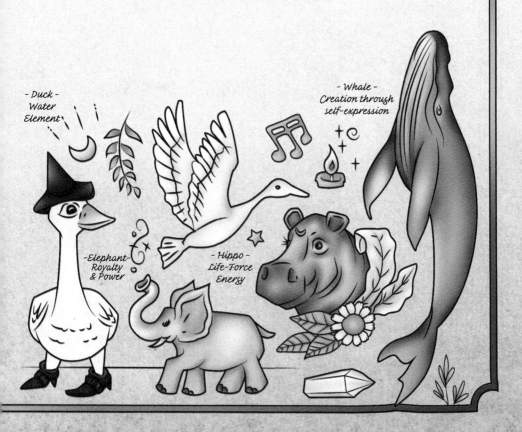

- Duck -
Water
Element

- Whale -
Creation through
self-expression

-Elephant-
Royalty
& Power

- Hippo -
Life-Force
Energy

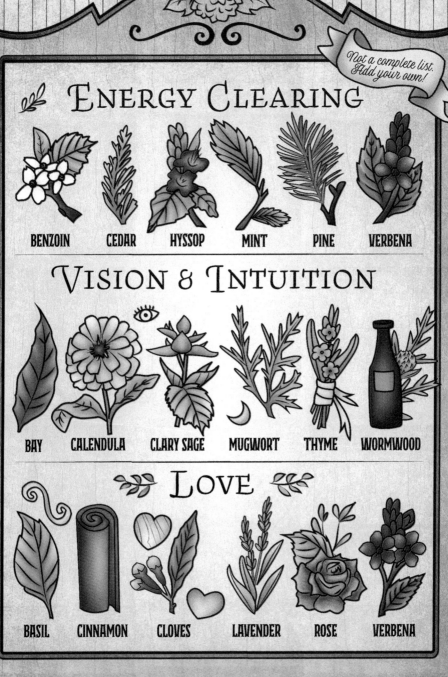

COMMON HERBS

PROTECTION

AGRIMONY **FENNEL** **HEATHER** **MULLEIN** **ROSEMARY** **RUE**
POISON

WITCH POWER

ACONITE **BELLADONNA** **BLACKTHORN** **HAWTHORN** **PARSLEY** **PERIWINKLE**
POISON POISON

SPIRITUALITY

BENZOIN **CYPRESS** **FRANKINCENSE** **MYRRH** **OAK** **YEW**

Not a complete list. Add your own!

& WITCH'S PLANTS

CRYSTAL MAGIC

CLEARING & RELEASING

AMAZONITE	BERYL	FUCHSITE	KYANITE	JET

ANTI-ANXIETY

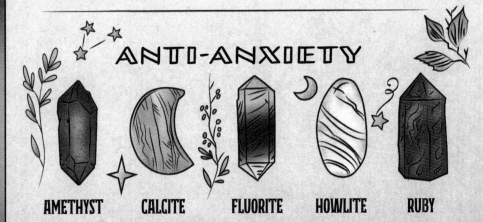

AMETHYST	CALCITE	FLUORITE	HOWLITE	RUBY

VISION & INTUITION

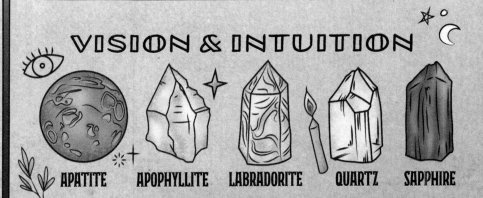

APATITE	APOPHYLLITE	LABRADORITE	QUARTZ	SAPPHIRE

& SYMBOLISM

CREATIVITY

AGATE	CARNELIAN	CITRINE	GARNET	SODALITE

MANIFESTATION

CINNABAR	JADE	JASPER	PERIDOT	TOPAZ

LOVE

PINK CALCITE	MOONSTONE	ROSE QUARTZ	SUGILITE	ZOISITE

DAYS OF THE WEEK

SUNDAY
SUN — YELLOW
Cast spells for success, friendship, and harmony.

MONDAY
MOON — WHITE
Cast spells for intuition, creativity, and healing.

TUESDAY
MARS — RED
Cast spells for confidence, strength, and protection.

WEDNESDAY
MERCURY — PURPLE
Cast spells for career, communication, and divination.

THURSDAY
JUPITER — BLUE
Cast spells for growth, prosperity, luck, and ambition.

FRIDAY
VENUS — GREEN
Cast spells for love, romance, beauty, and happiness.

SATURDAY
SATURN — BLACK
Cast spells for release, to break habits, and dispel negativity.

The days of the week correspond to ancient planetary symbolism and energy. While you might enjoy aligning yourself with the planetary power of specific days of the week for specific spells or intentions, this correspondence is entirely optional. Cast your magic on any day that feels appropriate and powerful to you and to your schedule.

HOURS OF THE DAY

MIDNIGHT
ALSO KNOWN AS THE WITCHING HOUR

Cast spells for letting go, completion, or starting over.

WITCHING HOUR*
Cast spells for spiritual connection and divination.

NIGHT
Cast spells for knowledge, wisdom, and creativity.

DAWN
Cast spells to start new things or add fresh energy.

DUSK
Cast spells for reflection, change, or release.

MORNING
Cast spells for growth, health, happiness, and abundance.

AFTERNOON
Cast spells for joy, friendship, harmony, or romance.

MID-DAY
Cast spells for strength, stamina, and power.

NIGHT

DAY

The time of day is another way you can align with magic, but do what feels right to you. You may not be a "night owl" and prefer to cast all of your spells at dawn. Or you might find power and pleasure in precisely lining up the moon phase, the season, the day of the week, and time of the day to cast your spells. Either method is correct, it all depends on you and how you prefer to work.

the correspondence of
THE MOON AND SEASONS

The moon completes a full cycle of its phases in just over 28 days, which is relatively quick. One moon cycle is perfect for shorter projects and immediate goals.

You can also "correspond" these shorter moon phases to a longer-term cycle, the seasons, also known as the Wheel of the Year. This longer cycle is useful for "big" goals and plans that'll take more than a month.

While the seasons and sun embody more of a conscious or outward energy, the moon is subconscious or internal. However, they both follow a similar cycle and progression of dark to light.

The handy chart on the following page demonstrates that the phases of the moon correspond to an energy point on the Wheel of the Year. This pattern of energy—the waxing and waning of light—is no coincidence. It's the pattern and flow of the creative force of the universe. This process and cycle is how magic "works."

Here's an overview of the eight sabbats and a chart that connects them to the moon phases and seasons.

IMBOLC: February 1 or 2. Imbolc is the time to celebrate the first signs of spring or the return of the sun's increasing light. This sabbat corresponds to the waxing crescent moon.

OSTARA: March 20. This sabbat is celebrated on the spring equinox. Witches often mark this day with a ritual planting of seeds. Ostara corresponds to the first quarter moon.

BELTANE: May 1. Beltane is a time for rituals of growth, creation, and taking action to make things happen. This sabbat corresponds to the waxing gibbous moon.

LITHA: June 20. This sabbat celebrates the summer solstice, when the sun is at its strongest. Litha is a time of great magical and personal power and corresponds to the full moon.

LUGHNASADH: August 1. This day is a celebration of the "first harvest" where we gather early grains, herbs, fruits, and vegetables from the earth. It corresponds to the waning gibbous moon, where light and power begin to descend from their fullest stage.

MABON: September 21. Celebrated on the autumnal equinox, this sabbat is about release, balance, and letting go. It is the second harvest and corresponds to the last quarter moon.

SAMHAIN: October 31. Samhain is a celebration of the dark half of the year. It is a time to cast spells of protection for the upcoming winter. It corresponds to the waning crescent moon.

YULE: December 21. Marked by the winter solstice and the shortest (darkest) day of the year, this sabbat corresponds to the dark and new moon.

A NOTE ABOUT THE CROSS-QUARTER DATES AND SOUTHERN HEMISPHERE SEASONS:

CROSS QUARTER DATES: The dates for the two solstices and two equinoxes each year—Ostara, Litha, Mabon, and Yule—are calculated astronomically, from the position of the earth to the sun. The "cross quarter" festivals, which are the points between—Imbolc, Beltane, Lughnasadh, and Samhain—are often celebrated on "fixed" dates instead of the actual midpoints. This book lists both the "Fixed Festival Dates," where it's more common to celebrate, and the "Astronomical Dates." Choose either date or any time in between for your own ritual. 'Tis the season for magic.

SOUTHERN HEMISPHERE SEASONS: If you're on the "southern" half of the Earth, like in Australia, the seasonal shifts are opposite on the calendar year. So you'll feel the energy of the summer solstice (corresponding to the full moon) in December instead of June, and so on.

THE SECRETS OF

YOUR FEELINGS ARE THE SECRET SAUCE

To make real magic happen, combine actions (things that you do), intentions (also known as feelings or emotions), as well as powers outside of yourself, such as the moon and nature. This chart will give you some ideas on how to feel and set your intentions.

An intention is when you strongly feel what you desire in your body, as if you already have it. You can use the phases of the moon to "pull the thread" of magic forward by listening to your feelings and continually refocusing these intentions with actions to match.

Since the moon and emotions are both linked to the subconscious, *you'll use your body to feel these things and set intentions,* not your thoughts in your conscious mind.

FIRST QUARTER - TOAD

Feel where you would like to change, grow, or expand. Allow yourself to dream and imagine what it might be like to make a change, even if it doesn't seem possible right now.

WAXING - RABBIT

Feel what excites you and sparks a sense of curiosity. Ask questions and look for answers, clues, patterns, and coincidences. Use the subtle feelings of what "lights you up" to set intentions and guide your actions.

NEW MOON - CAT

Allow yourself to feel where you are judging yourself. When you are ready, forgive yourself and let the energy shift until you find a place of neutrality and self-acceptance.

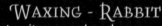

MOON MAGIC

FULL MOON - OWL

Reaffirm your visions and intentions until the energy of what you desire begins to feel real.

If you feel clarity, make decisions to move forward quickly.

If you feel confusion, illuminate your emotions through writing, ritual, divination, movement, etc.

Ask: What am I missing? What am I feeling?

LAST QUARTER - RAVEN

Allow yourself to feel what's working and what isn't. Let your feelings flow to a place of ease and trust in yourself, so you can discern what you want and what you do not want.

WANING - SNAKE

Feel the relief as you realize that some thoughts and feelings are unnecessary. Intend to let those things go, and then see what you have left. Let your intentions flow to a place of release.

DARK - BAT

Let the darkness filter out noise and distractions. Take a step back from actions and thoughts. Allow the dark moon to reset your mind, body, and spirit with the energy of rest.

MOON SIGNS

The Moon in the Zodiac

Alongside the moon's phases, our moon travels through the zodiac constellations in about 28 days. The moon transits through each individual zodiac sign for about two or three days. You can use these short cycles to hyper-focus your magic and intentions, if you wish.

You'll often hear the moon sign called out (full moon in Scorpio!) and the moon's transits are noted on the weekly calendars in this book.

Use these pages as a handy reference sheet to see if you can feel the intricacies of the moon as it transits through the zodiac signs.

MOON IN ARIES

A fire sign, the moon in Aries evokes a desire to start fresh. You may find you've got extra energy to get things done and start new projects. However, this moon is a better time to start (and complete) short-term projects rather than long-term projects or planning. Channel energy or frustrations into movement and child-like activities—art, sports, or other playful activities that you enjoy.

MOON IN TAURUS

An earth sign and the zodiac sign symbolizing the home, comfort, decor, and finances. The moon in Taurus is an optimal moon sign for starting long-term projects. You may feel called to spend time at home, in your garden, or in nature. This moon sign is an excellent time to ground yourself by meditating or contemplating your desires outdoors.

MOON IN GEMINI

An air sign, the moon in Gemini is an excellent time for thinking, learning, reading, pursuing curiosities and interests, focusing on mental activities, traveling, and talking with fascinating people. You may find that journaling or discussing deep topics with others will lead to rewarding insights and new perspectives when the moon is in Gemini.

MOON IN CANCER

A water sign, the moon in Cancer is a time to be at home, reflect, and get in touch with your feelings. You may feel called to focus on bonding with family or loved ones in intimate ways. Cooking and cleaning may be more appealing when the moon is in Cancer. Activities in or near water, like swimming or walking along the shore, can help you get in tune with your watery emotions.

MOON IN LEO

A fire sign, the moon in Leo is a time to focus on yourself and your creativity. It's a magical time to get in touch with your own intuition and listen for what your heart truly desires. Do, say, and be who you are without fear. Let yourself shine and take time to live, laugh, and love as passionately as you can. This moon sign can be an excellent time for dating. However, you may also prefer to spend it all on yourself.

MOON IN VIRGO

Virgo is the earth sign associated with organization, efficient habits, and health. A moon in Virgo is undoubtedly the best time to start a new routine or positive habit, or to organize, get on a schedule, or tidy things up. You may find that your mind is sharp, sensitive, and quick while the moon is in Virgo, so take this opportunity to catch up on your studies, read, or learn new things.

MOON IN LIBRA

An air sign of diplomacy, balance, and visual appeal. The moon in Libra can be an auspicious time to work on relationships, find balance, and socialize. You may also be called to let some things go, to regain harmony or release the weight of what holds you down while the moon is in Libra. The Libra moon is also a time to speak up, share, or write about topics you believe in.

MOON IN SCORPIO

A dark water sign, use the moon in Scorpio to "find" motivation, harness your own power, take control, and rid yourself of things that no longer serve you. You may find you've got the drive and power to work on your finances or speak your mind on things you typically are afraid to bring up. Use this moon time to pursue any of your passions or go deep into topics of importance.

MOON IN SAGITTARIUS

The fire sign of truth and visions, the moon in Sagittarius is a time to make long-term plans that take you in new directions, to think big, to use your imagination, and visualize a positive future. You may also want to plan a trip, do something you've always wanted to do, or speak your truth where you've held back.

MOON IN CAPRICORN

An earth sign, the moon in Capricorn is a time to focus on career, business, structure, careful use of resources, and practical achievement. You may also feel inspired to declutter, get rid of energy and possessions you no longer need, or to otherwise cut the excess and reprioritize what is truly important in your life.

MOON IN AQUARIUS

An air sign that symbolizes esoterica, freethinking, and personal freedom, the moon in Aquarius is an excellent time to expand your mind to find new, unexpected ideas and solutions. Think about what you can do to help humanity or how you can contribute to society. If you typically follow the pack, this is an auspicious time to go your own way.

MOON IN PISCES

The water sign of dreaming, psychic awareness, and intuition, the moon in Pisces is auspicious time for divination, reflection, mystical pursuits, and retreats into nature or water. The two fish of this sign signify the pull of our earthy desires vs. our spiritual pursuits, so take time to balance this with meditation, daydreaming, and getting in touch with your soul's calling.

THE ELEMENTS

SPIRIT

CONNECTION TO THE DIVINE SOURCE, DIVINE WITHIN, OR TRUE SELF.

WATER — EMOTION, INTUITION, AND CLEANSING RELEASE.

AIR — KNOWLEDGE, IDEAS, EXPANSION, AND COMMUNICATION.

EARTH — BELONGING, SECURITY, AND ABUNDANCE OF RESOURCES.

FIRE — CREATIVITY, LOVE, INSPIRATION, AND DESTROYING TO RE-CREATE.

- and the -

THE PENTACLE

Spellcasting Basics

There are opening and closing steps that are basic accompaniments to spells in this book. These steps are optional but advisable: at least know "why" many witches perform these processes and try them out for yourself.

And keep in mind, this is a super basic "coloring book" guide to the spellcasting process. There are books and online sources that go much further in-depth.

THE SECRET OF SPELLS

The secret to powerful spells is in you. Your feeling and vibration in alignment with your true source of self—and/or a higher power—is what makes spells work.

The secret isn't in having the right ingredients and doing all the steps in a particular order. It's in your ability to focus your intent and use your feelings, mind, and soul to call in what you want—to harness the energy of yourself in harmony with the Earth, stars, moon, planets, or whatever other spiritual forces you call upon.

BREAK THE RULES

The first rule is to throw out any of the rules that don't work for you. Do things that feel right, significant, and meaningful. Adapt spells from different practices, books, and teachers. The only way to know what works is to follow your curiosity and try things out.

USING TOOLS

Your feelings and vibration are what unlocks the magic, not the tools, exact words, or sequences. You can cast amazing spells for free with no tools at all, and you can cast an elaborate spell that yields no results.

That said, tools like herbs, oils, crystals, and cauldrons can be powerful and fun to use in your spells. Just don't feel pressured or discouraged if you don't have much to start. Keep your magic straightforward and powerful. The right tools and ingredients will come.

"AS ABOVE, SO BELOW"

Tools, ingredients, and symbols are based on the magical theory of sympathetic magic and correspondence. You might hear the phrase, "As Above, So Below," which means the spiritual qualities of objects are passed down to earth. It's "sympathetic magic," or "this equals that," like how a figure of a lion represents that power but is not an actual lion.

Start by following lists, charts, and spells to get a feel for what others use and then begin to discover your own meaningful symbolism and correspondences.

- Donkey -
Tenacity

PERMISSION

Spellbooks are like guidelines. They should be modified, simplified, or embellished to your liking. And don't degrade your magic by calling it "lazy." Keeping your witchcraft simple is okay. Go ahead, you have permission.

Also, it's not a competition to see who can use the most esoteric stuff in their spell. Hooray! It's about finding your personal power and style.

SPELLCASTING OUTLINE:

1. Plan and prepare.
2. Cast a circle.
3. Ground and center.
4. Invoke a deity or connection to self.
5. Raise energy.
6. Do your spellcraft (like the spells in this book).
7. Ground and center again.
8. Close your circle.
9. Clean up.
10. Act in accord (and be patient).

1. PLAN AND PREPARE: If you're doing a written spell, read it several times to get familiar with it. Decide if there's anything you'll substitute or change. If you're writing your own spell, enjoy the process and mystery of seeing the messages and theme come together.

Gather all of the items you'll be using (if any) and plan out the space and time where you'll do the spell. Spells can be impromptu, so preparations can be quick and casual if you like.

2. CAST A CIRCLE AND CALL THE QUARTERS: A magic circle is a container to collect the energy of your spell. Circles are also protective, as they form a ring or "barrier" around you. Circles can elevate your space to a higher vibration and clear out unwanted energy before you begin. Calling the Quarters is done to get the universal energies of the elements flowing. Incense is typically burned at the same time to purify the air and energy. If you

can't burn things, that's ok. If you've never cast a circle, try it. It's a mystical experience like no other. Once you have a few candles lit and start to walk around it, magic does happen!

HOW TO CAST A CIRCLE: This is a basic, bare-bones way to cast a circle. It's often much more elaborate, and this explanation barely does it justice, so read up to find out more. And note that while some cast the circle first and then call the Quarters, some do it the other way around.

1. Hold out your hand, wand, or crystal, and imagine a white light and a sphere of pure energy surrounding your space, as you circle around clockwise three times. Your circle can be large or it can be tiny, just space for you and your materials.

2. Call the Four Quarters or Five Points of the Pentagram, depending on your preferences. The Quarters (also known as the Elements!) are Earth (North), Air (East), Fire (South), and Water (West). Many use the Pentagram and also call the 5th Element, Spirit or Self.

Face in each direction and say a few words to welcome the element. For example, "To the North, I call upon the power of grounding and strength. To the East, I call upon the source of knowledge. To the South, I call upon the passion and burning desire to take action. To the West, I call upon the intuition of emotion. To the Spirit and Source of Self, I call upon the guidance and light."

3. GROUND AND CENTER: Grounding and centering prepare you to use the energy from the Earth, elements, and universe. Most witches agree that if you skip these steps, you'll be drawing off of your own energy, which can be exhausting and ineffective. It's wise to ground and center both before and after a spell. It's like the difference between being "plugged into" the magical energy of the Earth and universe versus "draining your batteries."

HOW TO GROUND AND CENTER:
To ground, imagine the energy coming up from the core of the Earth and into your feet, as you breathe deeply. You can visualize deep roots from your feet all the way into the center of the Earth, with these roots drawing the Earth's energy in and out of you. The point is to allow these great channels of energy to flow through you and into your spell. You can also imagine any of your negative energy, thoughts, or stress leaving.

To center, once you've got a good flow of energy from the ground, imagine the energy shining through and out the top of your head as a pure form of your highest creative self and then back in as the light of guidance. Suspend yourself here between the Earth and the sky, supported with the energy flowing freely through you, upheld, balanced, cleansed, and "in flow" with the energy of the universe. This process takes just a couple of minutes.

4. INVOKE A DEITY OR CREATIVE SOURCE: If you'd like to invoke a deity or your highest self to help raise energy and your vibration, call upon them. Invoking deities is way deeper than this book, so research it more if it calls to you!

5. RAISE ENERGY: The point of raising energy is to channel the universal (magical!) forces you tapped into through the previous steps to use in your spell. And raising energy is fun. You can sing, dance, chant, meditate, or do breath work. You want to do something that feels natural, so you can really get into it, lose yourself, and raise your state of consciousness.

A good way to start is to chant "Ong," allowing the roof of your mouth to vibrate ever so slightly. This vibration changes up the energy in your mind, body, and breath and is a simple yet powerful technique.

Another tip is to raise energy to the point of the "peak" where you feel it at its highest. Don't go too far where you start to tucker out or lose enthusiasm!

6. DO YOUR SPELL: Your spell can be as simple as saying an intention and focusing on achieving the outcome of what you want, or it can be more elaborate. Whichever way you prefer, do what feels right to you.

TIPS ON VISUALIZATION AND INTENTION:
Most spellwork involves a bit of imagination and intention, and here are some subtleties you can explore.

The Power of You The most important tool in magic is you. You've got it—both power right now and vast untapped power that you can explore. To cast a successful spell, you've got to focus your mind and genuinely feel the emotions and feelings of the things you want to manifest.

If you haven't started meditating in some form yet, start now! It's not too late, and it's easier than you think.

Visualize the Outcome

Visualization doesn't have to be visual. In fact, *feeling* the outcome of what you want may be more effective than seeing it (try both). And try to feel or see the *completion* of your desire without worrying about the process or *how* you'll get there.

If you don't know how you're going to achieve your goal (yet!), it can feel overwhelming when you try to visualize how you're going to pull it off. Instead, feel the sense of calm, completion, and control that you'll feel *after* you achieve it.

Phrase it Positively

Another tip is to phrase your intentions and desires positively. You're putting energy into this, so make sure the intention is going to be good for you. Instead of saying what you don't want, "to get out of my bad job that I hate," phrase it positively, "I want to do something that's fulfilling with my career."

Then you'll be able to feel good about it as you visualize and cast your spell.

7. GROUND AND CENTER AGAIN

After your spell, it's important to ground out any excess energy. Do this again by visualizing energy flowing through you and out. You can also imagine any "extra" energy you have petering out as you release it back into the Earth.

8. CLOSE YOUR CIRCLE

If you called the Quarters or a deity, let them know the spell has ended by calling them out again, with thanks if desired.

Close your circle the opposite of how you opened it, circling around three times or more counterclockwise. Then say, "This circle is closed," or do a closing chant or song to finish your spell.

9. CLEAN UP

Don't be messy with your magic! Put away all of your spell items.

10. ACT IN ACCORD: Once you have cast your spell, you've got to take action. You can cast a spell to become a marine biologist, but if you don't study for it, it's never going to happen. So take action towards what you want to open the possibility for it to come.

Look for signs, intuition, and coincidences that point you in the direction of your desires. If you get inspired after a spell, take action! Don't be surprised if you ask for money and then come up with a new idea to make money. Follow those clues, especially if they feel exciting and good.

If your spell comes true, discard and "release" any charm bag, poppet, or item you used to hold and amplify energy. Also, give thanks (if that's in your practice) or repay the universe in some way, doing something kind or of service that you feel is a solid trade for what you received from your spell.

WHAT IF YOUR SPELL DOESN'T WORK?

It's true that not all spells will work! But sometimes the results just take longer than you'd like, so be patient.

If your spell doesn't work, you can use divination or meditation to do some digging into reasons why.

The good news is your own magic, power, frequency, and intention is still on your side. You can try again and add more energy in the direction of your desired outcome by casting another spell.

Give it some deep thought. What else is at play? Did you really take inspired action? Are you totally honest with yourself about what you want? Are there any thoughts or feelings about your spell that feel "off"? Are you grateful for what you already have? Can you "give back" or reciprocate with service or energy?

FOR MORE TIPS AND INSPIRATION:

Seek out websites, books, podcasts, and videos on spirituality. Follow your intuition and curiosity to deepen your practice and find your own style. And check out other books in the *Coloring Book of Shadows* series, like the *Book of Spells* and *Witch Life*.

SOUTHERN HEMISPHERE MAGIC

If you're in the Southern Hemisphere in a place like Australia, there are a couple of differences that you'll need to note.

The biggest difference is that since seasonal shifts are opposite on the calendar year, you'll feel the energy of Samhain around May 1 instead of October 31.

Southern Hemisphere "spinning and circle casting" will go "sun wise" according to the south—counterclockwise for invoking (drawing in), clockwise for banishing (letting go).

North and South Elements are also typically swapped in Southern Hemisphere magic—North = Fire, South = Earth.

SO MOTE IT BE.

Your Magical Vision

AND PLANS FOR THIS YEAR:

Remember that plans almost always change. And... *Spoiler alert!*
You can't control anything, but you can influence, change, and
make all sorts of things better for yourself and for the world. You
matter, and your magic and energy matter.

- Who do you want to be this year?
- What do you want this year to feel like?
- What do you want to take action on or work towards?
- What do you want to leave behind?
- What steps, thoughts, actions, and feelings will get you going in
the direction that you desire?
- What does success feel and look like to you?
- What do you really want that you are hesitant to ask for?

WITH WINGS TO SOAR,
OWL'S EYES TO SEE YOUR DREAMS,
THE STRENGTH OF A BEAR,
THE CLEVERNESS OF A FOX,
AND THE COURAGE OF A LION...

SO IT SHALL BE!

- Eagle-
Spiritual Power

1ST HALF 2025

January

S	M	T	W	Th	F	Sa
			1	2	3	4
5	◐	7	8	9	10	11
12	○	14	15	16	17	18
19	20	◑	22	23	24	25
26	27	28	●	30	31	

February

S	M	T	W	Th	F	Sa
						1
2	3	4	◐	6	7	8
9	10	11	○	13	14	15
16	17	18	19	◐	21	22
23	24	25	26	●	28	

March

S	M	T	W	Th	F	Sa
						1
2	3	4	5	◐	7	8
9	10	11	12	13	○	15
16	17	18	19	20	21	◑
23	24	25	26	27	28	●
30	31					

April

S	M	T	W	Th	F	Sa
		1	2	3	◐	5
6	7	8	9	10	11	○
13	14	15	16	17	18	19
◑	21	22	23	24	25	26
●	28	29	30			

May

S	M	T	W	Th	F	Sa
				1	2	3
◐	5	6	7	8	9	10
11	○	13	14	15	16	17
18	19	◑	21	22	23	24
25	●	27	28	29	30	31

June

S	M	T	W	Th	F	Sa
1	◐	3	4	5	6	7
8	9	10	○	12	13	14
15	16	17	◑	19	20	21
22	23	24	●	26	27	28
29	30					

2ND HALF 2025

July

S	M	T	W	Th	F	Sa
		1	◐	3	4	5
6	7	8	9	○	11	12
13	14	15	16	◑	18	19
20	21	22	23	●	25	26
27	28	29	30	31		

August

S	M	T	W	Th	F	Sa
					◐	2
3	4	5	6	7	8	○
10	11	12	13	14	15	◑
17	18	19	20	21	22	●
24	25	26	27	28	29	30
◖						

September

S	M	T	W	Th	F	Sa
	1	2	3	4	5	6
○	8	9	10	11	12	13
◑	15	16	17	18	19	20
●	22	23	24	25	26	27
28	◐	30				

October

S	M	T	W	Th	F	Sa
			1	2	3	4
5	○	7	8	9	10	11
12	◑	14	15	16	17	18
19	20	●	22	23	24	25
26	27	28	◐	30	31	

November

S	M	T	W	Th	F	Sa
						1
2	3	4	○	6	7	8
9	10	11	◑	13	14	15
16	17	18	19	●	21	22
23	24	25	26	27	◐	29
30						

December

S	M	T	W	Th	F	Sa
	1	2	3	○	5	6
7	8	9	10	◑	12	13
14	15	16	17	18	●	20
21	22	23	24	25	26	◐
28	29	30	31			

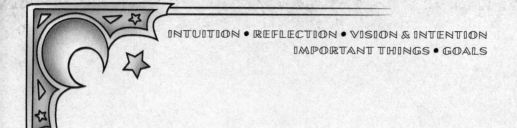

INTUITION • REFLECTION • VISION & INTENTION
IMPORTANT THINGS • GOALS

Skulls represent magic and possibility
between dark and light, life and death.

THIS MONTH:

Full Moon in Cancer: January 13
Sun enters Aquarius: January 19
New Moon in Aquarius: January 29
Uranus Retrograde Ends: January 30

Listen to your spirit in silence and darkness.

Jet shifts energy from subconscious to conscious.

Burn wormwood and sandalwood to communicate with the spirit world.

Cedar will help you connect to wisdom from spirit.

JANUARY
THE MAGIC OF OWL

Owl is a messenger, sharing secrets of magic and spirit.
Owl knows the power in your shadows.
Ask Owl how you can reveal your hidden powers.

Sit with the energy of Owl for 90 seconds.

What message did you receive from Owl?

CANDLES
symbolize light & spirit
illuminating the darkness.

THE MOON
Observe the moon's phases to
connect to the rhythm of the night.

BAY
Bay's scent attunes you to
your psychic sensitivities.

SAGE
brings wisdom to turn
desires into reality.

THE NIGHT
Notice what you feel in the dark,
within yourself and without.

LABRADORITE
embodies the polarity of dark and light:
the power of alchemical transmutation.

LEARNING OWL'S MAGIC
REVEAL THE POWER OF YOUR SHADOWS

Owls are keepers of wisdom, truth, and magic. Their exceptional hearing and vision give them keen awareness to sense what others cannot—especially in darkness. You can't hide from Owl. She sees you and she sees what's hidden in your shadows. Your "shadows" often obscure possibilities, opportunities, and desires of your soul that are repressed because of shame or fear.

Connect to Owl's "shadow sight" and uncover these hidden gems and untapped powers within you in this simple spell:

Find a dark, quiet place at night. Go into nature where owls are found, or sit outside, or in a dark room with an open window. Be still and silent. Listen or sense for owls and other nocturnal creatures. These "night sounds" will encourage your senses to heighten.

Invite the presence of Owl. Then speak or feel these words or sentiments of your own:

"Darkest moon to full moon's light, I reclaim the gift of Owl's sight. With Owl's silent, watchful eyes, my hidden powers wake and rise."

Quickly, and from the "knowing" feeling of your intuitive body, answer these questions:
1. What do you desire that you think you cannot have?
2. Why do you think you cannot have it?
3. If it was possible for you, how could it be possible?

You'll know you've uncovered a "shadow" or hidden power when the answers to these questions give a sudden spark or glimmer within your energetic body. Once you feel that spark of magic, imagine or think about the golden eyes of Owl. This vision of Owl will imprint within you. Recall it when you need a reminder of Owl magic.

JANUARY 2025

Place amethyst, lapis lazuli, or mugwort under your pillow to evoke empowering dreams.

	SUNDAY	MONDAY	TUESDAY
	29	30 New Moon ● ♑	31
	5	6 First Quarter ◑	7
	12	13 Full Moon ○ ♋	14
	19 ☉ Sun in Aquarius ♒	20	21 Last Quarter ◑
	26	27	28

WEDNESDAY	THURSDAY	FRIDAY	SATURDAY
1	2	3	4
8	9	10	11
15	16	17	18
22	23	24	25
			★ Imbolc (Fixed Date)
29 New Moon ● ≈	30	31	1

DECEMBER 2024/JANUARY 2025

MONDAY, DECEMBER 30, 2024
New (Black) Moon ● ♑ 5:27 PM EST

TUESDAY, DECEMBER 31, 2024

WEDNESDAY, JANUARY 1
► Moon void-of-course begins 1:01 AM EST
Moon enters Aquarius ♒ 5:49 AM EST

THURSDAY, JANUARY 2
► Moon void-of-course begins 11:13 PM EST

FRIDAY, JANUARY 3
Moon enters Pisces ♓ 10:20 AM EST

SATURDAY, JANUARY 4

SUNDAY, JANUARY 5
► Moon void-of-course begins 9:30 AM EST
Moon enters Aries ♈ 2:01 PM EST

*Burn patchouli, myrrh, rose, or sage as an offering to
Athena, Greek Goddess of wisdom, crafts, and heroism.*

JANUARY 2025

MONDAY, JANUARY 6
First Quarter ☽ 6:57 PM EST

TUESDAY, JANUARY 7
►Moon void-of-course begins 4:16 PM EST
Moon enters Taurus ♉ 5:11 PM EST

WEDNESDAY, JANUARY 8

THURSDAY, JANUARY 9
►Moon void-of-course begins 5:50 PM EST
Moon enters Gemini ♊ 8:07 PM EST

FRIDAY, JANUARY 10

SATURDAY, JANUARY 11
►Moon void-of-course begins 7:04 PM EST
Moon enters Cancer ♋ 11:23 PM EST

SUNDAY, JANUARY 12

LISTEN

*When do you feel
your magic? What
gives you power?*

JANUARY 2025

MONDAY, JANUARY 13
Full Moon ○ ♋ 5:27 PM EST
►Moon void-of-course begins 11:46 PM EST

TUESDAY, JANUARY 14
Moon enters Leo ♌ 4:12 AM EST

WEDNESDAY, JANUARY 15
►Moon void-of-course begins 11:10 PM EST

THURSDAY, JANUARY 16
Moon enters Virgo ♍ 11:46 AM EST

Use only ethically sourced skulls, bones, horns, and feathers.

FRIDAY, JANUARY 17

SATURDAY, JANUARY 18
►Moon void-of-course begins 9:02 PM EST
Moon enters Libra ♎ 10:32 PM EST

SUNDAY, JANUARY 19
☉ Sun enters Aquarius ♒ 2:59 PM EST

Contemplate a rose to hear messages from your spirit. Gold roses symbolize the moon and divine wisdom.

JANUARY 2025

MONDAY, JANUARY 20
►Moon void-of-course begins 11:34 PM EST

TUESDAY, JANUARY 21
Moon enters Scorpio ♏ 11:20 AM EST
Last Quarter ◐ 3:31 PM EST

WEDNESDAY, JANUARY 22

THURSDAY, JANUARY 23
►Moon void-of-course begins 7:04 PM EST
Moon enters Sagittarius ♐ 11:29 PM EST

FRIDAY, JANUARY 24

SATURDAY, JANUARY 25

SUNDAY, JANUARY 26
► Moon void-of-course begins 4:40 AM EST
Moon enters Capricorn ♑ 8:43 AM EST

FEATHERS

Use an owl feather to trace a magic circle and increase your psychic vision.

JANUARY 2025/FEBRUARY 2025

MONDAY, JANUARY 27

TUESDAY, JANUARY 28
► Moon void-of-course begins 10:49 AM EST
Moon enters Aquarius ♒ 2:32 PM EST

WEDNESDAY, JANUARY 29
New Moon ● ♒ 7:36 AM EST

THURSDAY, JANUARY 30
► Moon void-of-course begins 6:29 AM EST
Moon enters Pisces ♓ 5:52 PM EST
♅℞ Uranus Retrograde ends

FRIDAY, JANUARY 31

SATURDAY, FEBRUARY 1
★ Imbolc (Fixed Festival Date)
► Moon void-of-course begins 5:05 PM EST
Moon enters Aries ♈ 8:10 PM EST

SUNDAY, FEBRUARY 2

IMBOLC

*Feel the magic of a fresh start. Try bathing or
cleaning with enlivening herbs (basil or mint) and
purifying herbs (agrimony and witch hazel.)*

CROCODILE

Channel crocodile to feel the depths of your power.

Water Lilies represent the power to begin again.

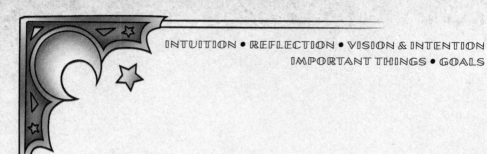

*Drink lemon balm tea to
ground and refresh yourself.*

THIS MONTH:

Imbolc: February 1-3
Jupiter Retrograde Ends: February 4
Full Moon in Leo: February 12
Sun enters Pisces: February 18
Mars Retrograde Ends: February 23
New Moon in Pisces: February 27

Sit with the energy of Cat for 90 seconds.

What message did you receive from Cat?

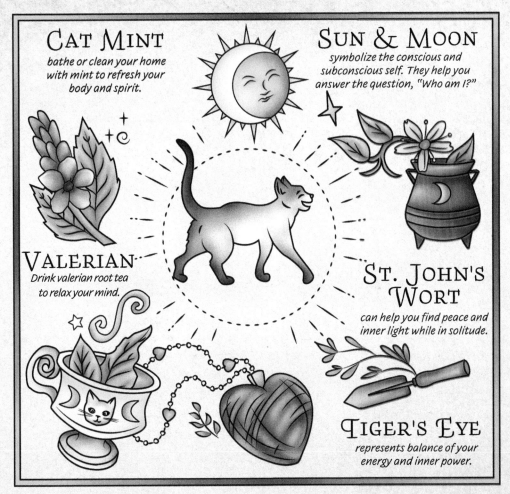

CAT MINT
bathe or clean your home with mint to refresh your body and spirit.

SUN & MOON
symbolize the conscious and subconscious self. They help you answer the question, "Who am I?"

VALERIAN
Drink valerian root tea to relax your mind.

ST. JOHN'S WORT
can help you find peace and inner light while in solitude.

TIGER'S EYE
represents balance of your energy and inner power.

LEARNING CAT'S MAGIC
CURIOSITY AND COMFORT

Cats symbolize magic, occult knowledge, and witchcraft. They are witches' familiars, shape-shifters, and represent the power of self-knowledge. "Cat magic" can show you how to embrace your authentic self by indulging in what brings you both curiosity and comfort.

SPELLWORK: An altar is a place to bring the spiritual into the material world—As Above, So Below. Altars speak to your subconscious in a way that's deeper than words or rational thought. This can help you uncover feelings or powers within yourself that may yet be indescribable.

Create an altar that represents the true essence of yourself. Add elements that represent "comfort" to you—herbs, crystals, symbols, deities, or hobbies that you enjoy, as well as elements that represent curiosity... what is not

yet familiar to you, but calls to you? These are the two opposite sides of "Cat magic."

For a more traditional balanced altar, place a black candle and shadowy things on one side to represent curiosities and things not yet fully realized. Place a white candle and "light" symbolism to represent your "comfort" and light that is already known to you. Or choose to arrange it in whatever way that feels right.

While it's fine to look outward for inspiration, listen to the language of your soul and pick colors, scents, deities, and symbols that are uniquely yours. Add a cat statue or picture of a favorite kitty to help bring "Cat energy" into your magic.

Consecrate your altar with incense, and embrace your full self—both what is familiar to you now and the curiosity of what is yet to be discovered.

FEBRUARY 2025

	SUNDAY	MONDAY	TUESDAY
	26	27	28
	2	★ Imbolc 9:11 AM EST 3	4
	9	10	11
	16	17	☉ Sun enters Pisces ♓ 18
	23	24	25

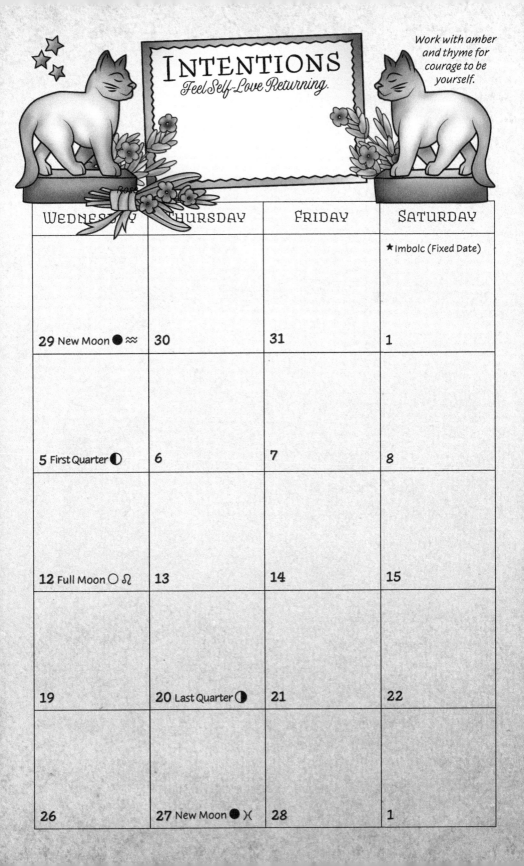

INTENTIONS
Feel Self-Love Returning.

Work with amber and thyme for courage to be yourself.

WEDNESDAY	THURSDAY	FRIDAY	SATURDAY
			★ Imbolc (Fixed Date)
29 New Moon ● ≈	**30**	**31**	**1**
5 First Quarter ◑	**6**	**7**	**8**
12 Full Moon ○ ♌	**13**	**14**	**15**
19	**20** Last Quarter ◑	**21**	**22**
26	**27** New Moon ● ♓	**28**	**1**

FEBRUARY 2025

MONDAY, FEBRUARY 3
► Moon void-of-course begins 5:20 AM EST
★ Imbolc (Astronomical Date) 9:11 AM EST
Moon enters Taurus ♉ 10:34 PM EST

TUESDAY, FEBRUARY 4
♃℞ Jupiter Retrograde ends

WEDNESDAY, FEBRUARY 5
First Quarter ☽ 3:01 AM EST
► Moon void-of-course begins 10:30 PM EST

THURSDAY, FEBRUARY 6
Moon enters Gemini ♊ 1:43 AM EST

FRIDAY, FEBRUARY 7

SATURDAY, FEBRUARY 8
► Moon void-of-course begins 2:52 AM EST
Moon enters Cancer ♋ 6:04 AM EST

SUNDAY, FEBRUARY 9

BASTET
Egyptian Goddess of Cats.
Offer Bastet water, milk, catnip, floral scents,
or meat. Or make a donation to help cats.

FEBRUARY 2025

MONDAY, FEBRUARY 10
► Moon void-of-course begins 8:50 AM EST
Moon enters Leo ♌ 12:01 PM EST

TUESDAY, FEBRUARY 11

WEDNESDAY, FEBRUARY 12
Full Moon ○ ♌ 8:54 AM EST
► Moon void-of-course begins 2:12 PM EST
Moon enters Virgo ♍ 8:06 PM EST

THURSDAY, FEBRUARY 13

FRIDAY, FEBRUARY 14

SATURDAY, FEBRUARY 15
► Moon void-of-course begins 3:36 AM EST
Moon enters Libra ♎ 6:45 AM EST

SUNDAY, FEBRUARY 16

WHISKERS

If you find a cat's whisker, place it on your altar to evoke curiosity.

FEBRUARY 2025

MONDAY, FEBRUARY 17
▸ Moon void-of-course begins 6:24 PM EST
Moon enters Scorpio ♏ 7:19 PM EST

TUESDAY, FEBRUARY 18
⊙ Sun enters Pisces ♓ 5:06 AM EST

WEDNESDAY, FEBRUARY 19

THURSDAY, FEBRUARY 20
▸ Moon void-of-course begins 5:06 AM EST
Moon enters Sagittarius ♐ 7:55 AM EST
Last Quarter ◑ 12:33 PM EST

FRIDAY, FEBRUARY 21

SATURDAY, FEBRUARY 22
▸ Moon void-of-course begins 3:39 PM EST
Moon enters Capricorn ♑ 6:09 PM EST

SUNDAY, FEBRUARY 23
♂℞ Mars Retrograde ends

*Moonstone and jasmine can help you
cultivate self-love, clarity, and inner peace.*

FEBRUARY/MARCH 2025

MONDAY, FEBRUARY 24
▸ Moon void-of-course begins 10:28 PM EST

TUESDAY, FEBRUARY 25
Moon enters Aquarius ♒ 12:39 AM EST

WEDNESDAY, FEBRUARY 26
▸ Moon void-of-course begins 5:04 PM EST

THURSDAY, FEBRUARY 27
Moon enters Pisces ♓ 3:47 AM EST
New Moon ● ♓ 7:45 PM EST

FRIDAY, FEBRUARY 28

SATURDAY, MARCH 1
▸ Moon void-of-course begins 3:05 AM EST
Moon enters Aries ♈ 4:51 AM EST
♀℞ Venus Retrograde begins (ends April 12)

SUNDAY, MARCH 2
▸ Moon void-of-course begins 8:51 AM EST

RACCOON

*Channel Raccoon's
magic to become
adaptable.*

*Sit in stillness and soothe your soul
with a cup of nettle tea.*

THIS MONTH:

Venus Retrograde: March 1-April 12
Full Moon in Virgo: March 14
Lunar Eclipse: March 14
Mercury Retrograde: March 15-April 7
Ostara (Spring Equinox): March 20
Sun enters Aries: March 20
New Moon in Aries: March 29
Partial Solar Eclipse: March 29

Take a big leap of action towards your intentions.

Make a wish as you blow the seeds off a dandelion puff.

Calcite can help you summon energy to move forward.

MARCH
THE MAGIC OF RABBIT
Rabbit will show you the balance, polarity, and wisdom that lies between stillness and taking action.
Ask Rabbit if it's time to stay still or time to move.

Sit with the energy of Rabbit for 90 seconds.

What message did you receive from Rabbit?

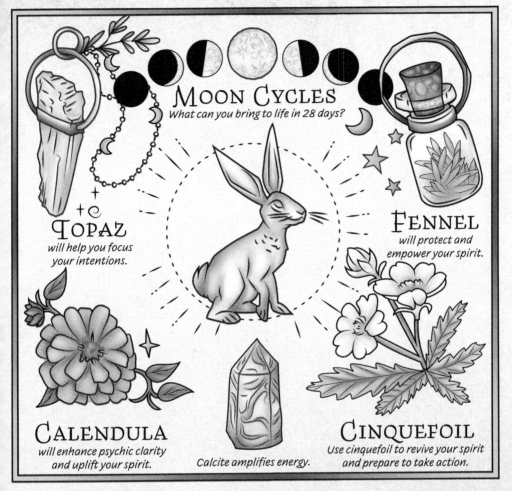

MOON CYCLES
What can you bring to life in 28 days?

TOPAZ
*will help you focus
your intentions.*

FENNEL
*will protect and
empower your spirit.*

CALENDULA
*will enhance psychic clarity
and uplift your spirit.*

Calcite amplifies energy.

CINQUEFOIL
*Use cinquefoil to revive your spirit
and prepare to take action.*

LEARNING RABBIT'S MAGIC
INTENTION AND ACTION IN THE FACE OF FEAR

There is potent magic and power in the polarity between staying still and moving forward. Rabbits can make great leaps quickly from statue-like stillness. Their secret? Intention. Intention combined with action is power—even in the face of fear.

PREPARE: Think deeply about changes that you might desire. How do you want to "leap" or grow? This is your intention. Write it down.

Then write down any fears or hesitations that have been holding you back or keeping you "still." Periods of stillness are essential in life, and fear is normal and won't necessarily go away, even if you face it. But you don't have to stay "stuck" in stillness or fear when you'd like to leap like Rabbit... and move yourself forward.

PERFORM THE RITUAL: In your third eye, deeply feel your intention. Immerse yourself in the feeling or energy of already having what you desire. Imagine yourself as a rabbit leaping over and through your fears. Spend a few minutes to connect to this sensation of action. Then bring the feeling to the lower back of your head. If your neck gets tingly—awesome.

TAKE ONE ACTION: Your magical guidance (intuition) will always show you at least one step to take in the direction that you want to go. This next step is already in your physical realm and you already know what it is... so take that leap.

KEEP GOING: Rabbits are biologically synced with the 28 day moon cycle. Use this next moon cycle to take action towards your intentions, even in the face of fear. Recall the energy of Rabbit to move forward... and leap!

MARCH 2025

	SUNDAY	MONDAY	TUESDAY
	23	24	25
	2	3	4
	9	10	11
	16	17	18
	23	24	25
	30	31	1

INTENTIONS
Take quick action.

WEDNESDAY	THURSDAY	FRIDAY	SATURDAY
26	27 New Moon ● ♓	28	1
5	6 First Quarter ◑	7 Lunar Eclipse	8
12	13	14 Full Moon ○ ♍	15
19	20 ★ Ostara (Spring Equinox) ☉ Sun enters Aries ♈	21	22 Last Quarter ◑
26	27	28 Partial Solar Eclipse	29 New Moon ● ♈
2	3	4 First Quarter ◑	5

MARCH 2025

MONDAY, MARCH 3
Moon enters Taurus ♉ 6:37 AM EST

TUESDAY, MARCH 4

WEDNESDAY, MARCH 5
► Moon void-of-course begins 6:54 AM EST
Moon enters Gemini ♊ 8:30 AM EST

THURSDAY, MARCH 6
First Quarter ◑ 12:32 PM EST

FRIDAY, MARCH 7
► Moon void-of-course begins 10:57 AM EST
Moon enters Cancer ♋ 12:29 PM EST

SATURDAY, MARCH 8

SUNDAY, MARCH 9
► Moon void-of-course begins 5:32 PM EDT
Moon enters Leo ♌ 6:58 PM EDT

*Sip ginger and citrus tea to ignite your spirit,
enliven your senses, and stoke the fire of action.*

MARCH 2025

MONDAY, MARCH 10

TUESDAY, MARCH 11
▸ Moon void-of-course begins 4:16 PM EDT

WEDNESDAY, MARCH 12
Moon enters Virgo ♍ 3:56 AM EDT

THURSDAY, MARCH 13

FRIDAY, MARCH 14
Full Moon ○ ♍ 2:55 AM EDT
Lunar Eclipse 2:59 AM EDT
▸ Moon void-of-course begins 1:48 PM EDT
Moon enters Libra ♎ 2:59 PM EDT

SATURDAY, MARCH 15
☿℞ Mercury Retrograde begins (ends April 7)

SUNDAY, MARCH 16
▸ Moon void-of-course begins 5:53 AM EDT

CARROT

*Carrots root
your intentions
with energy and
ambition.*

MARCH 2025

MONDAY, MARCH 17
Moon enters Scorpio ♏ 3:31 AM EDT

TUESDAY, MARCH 18

WEDNESDAY, MARCH 19
► Moon void-of-course begins 3:29 PM EDT
Moon enters Sagittarius ♐ 4:17 PM EDT

THURSDAY, MARCH 20
★ Ostara (Spring Equinox) 5:01 AM EDT
☉ Sun enters Aries ♈ 5:01 AM EDT

FRIDAY, MARCH 21

SATURDAY, MARCH 22
► Moon void-of-course begins 2:53 AM EDT
Moon enters Capricorn ♑ 3:29 AM EDT
Last Quarter ◐ 7:30 AM EDT

SUNDAY, MARCH 23

OSTARA

Feel the energy of exciting new possibilities.
Drink tea, burn incense, or bathe with herbs like
mugwort, rose, calendula, and jasmine.

MARCH 2025

MONDAY, MARCH 24
▸ Moon void-of-course begins 11:00 AM EDT
Moon enters Aquarius ♒ 11:24 AM EDT

TUESDAY, MARCH 25

WEDNESDAY, MARCH 26
▸ Moon void-of-course begins 6:15 AM EDT
Moon enters Pisces ♓ 3:31 PM EDT

THURSDAY, MARCH 27

FRIDAY, MARCH 28
▸ Moon void-of-course begins 4:30 PM EDT
Moon enters Aries ♈ 4:36 PM EDT

SATURDAY, MARCH 29
Partial Solar Eclipse 6:47 AM EDT
New Moon ● ♈ 6:58 AM EDT

SUNDAY, MARCH 30
▸ Moon void-of-course begins 5:17 AM EDT
Moon enters Taurus ♉ 4:16 PM EDT

DANCE

Mimic Rabbit's quick, playful movements to invoke agility and action.

MARCH/APRIL 2025

MONDAY, MARCH 31

TUESDAY, APRIL 1
► Moon void-of-course begins 1:43 PM EDT
Moon enters Gemini Ⅱ 4:26 PM EDT

WEDNESDAY, APRIL 2

THURSDAY, APRIL 3
► Moon void-of-course begins 2:26 PM EDT
Moon enters Cancer ♋ 6:49 PM EDT

FRIDAY, APRIL 4
First Quarter ◑ 10:14 PM EDT

SATURDAY, APRIL 5
► Moon void-of-course begins 6:55 PM EDT

SUNDAY, APRIL 6
Moon enters Leo ♌ 12:34 AM EDT

EDIBLE FLOWERS

Sprinkle edible flower petals like calendula, borage, pansy, and nasturtium onto your salads to bring the magic of the wild into your meal.

SKUNK

Visualize Skunk's bold confidence to strengthen your aura.

*Enhance your clarity and efficiency with
"Rat Magic" by organizing your space.*

THIS MONTH:

Mercury Retrograde Ends: April 7
Full Moon in Libra: April 12
Venus Retrograde Ends: April 12
Sun enters Taurus: April 19
New Moon in Taurus: April 27

Enliven & clarify your spirit with parsley & lemon tea.

Figs represent an abundance of resources.

Stick pins into a lemon and hang it as a charm for luck and energy.

Mushrooms represent faeries and magic.

APRIL
THE MAGIC OF RAT

Rat will show you that you are capable of organizing and planning for success.
Ask Rat for insight on planning and prospering.

Sit with the energy of Rat for 90 seconds.

What message did you receive from Rat?

Invoke Rat magic to strategize for success.

CINNABAR
Manifestation & abundance.

HAZEL
Cast an empowering magic circle with a hazelwood stick.

CUNNING
A little planning goes a long way!

JASPER
Channel strength and endurance to keep going.

NUTMEG
Sip nutmeg tea to enhance your intuition & manifest your desires.

LEARNING RAT'S MAGIC
REMEMBERING THAT YOU ARE CAPABLE

Rat magic lies in capability, organization, adaptability, attention to detail, and shrewd intelligence. These qualities make Rat a master of resourcefulness. These spells will help you to remember that you are capable of success, too.

Cleaning Rituals: A clean, organized space will cultivate clarity and focus to pursue your goals.

Plan out what you need to do, then take action on the most important tasks, such as clearing out what is no longer needed.

Diffuse essential oils, light candles, or simmer a pot of water and aromatic herbs to set a magical tone. Feel as though you are a cunning, empowered, and delightfully witchy little rat as you busy yourself with the details of organizing your resources.

Create a "Ratty Success" Charm Bag: Gather a small pouch or a jar with a lid and place the following items inside it: Write down your intentions alongside a little note about how shrewd, cunning, and clever you are. Add a pinch of dried basil for prosperity, grains of rice for abundance, a bay leaf for wisdom, and a piece of quartz for clarity. Add a small symbol of a rat, such as a charm or drawing.

Hold your ratty charm bag and enchant it by feeling the satisfaction of reaching your goals. Feel the energy of success flowing through you and into the charm. Say or write the affirmation:

Like Rat, so clever and keen, I sort my life and set the scene. With plans well laid, I know what I'll do, I'll adapt with tenacity, through and through.

This "Rat magic" charm bag will remind you that you are cunning, intelligent, and capable.

APRIL 2025

	SUNDAY	MONDAY	TUESDAY
	30	31	1
	6	7	8
	13	14	15
	20 Last Quarter ◑	21	22
	27 New Moon ● ♉	28	29

WEDNESDAY	THURSDAY	FRIDAY	SATURDAY
2	3	4 First Quarter ◑	5
9	10	11	12 Full Moon ○ ♎
			☉ Sun enters Taurus
16	17	18	19
23	24	25	26
	★ Beltane (Fixed Date)		
30	1	2	3

APRIL 2025

MONDAY, APRIL 7
☿℞ Mercury Retrograde ends

TUESDAY, APRIL 8
► Moon void-of-course begins 12:09 AM EDT
Moon enters Virgo ♍ 9:40 AM EDT

WEDNESDAY, APRIL 9

THURSDAY, APRIL 10
► Moon void-of-course begins 3:49 PM EDT
Moon enters Libra ♎ 9:12 PM EDT

FRIDAY, APRIL 11

SATURDAY, APRIL 12
Full Moon ○ ♎ 8:23 PM EDT
♀℞ Venus Retrograde ends

SUNDAY, APRIL 13
► Moon void-of-course begins 6:01 AM EDT
Moon enters Scorpio ♏ 9:54 AM EDT

Create a bundle of herbs like basil, mint, fruit blossom, and cloves to manifest abundance.

APRIL 2025

MONDAY, APRIL 14

TUESDAY, APRIL 15
► Moon void-of-course begins 10:24 PM EDT
Moon enters Sagittarius ♐ 10:38 PM EDT

WEDNESDAY, APRIL 16

THURSDAY, APRIL 17

FRIDAY, APRIL 18
► Moon void-of-course begins 7:38 AM EDT
Moon enters Capricorn ♑ 10:12 AM EDT

SATURDAY, APRIL 19
☉ Sun enters Taurus ♉ 3:55 PM EDT

SUNDAY, APRIL 20
► Moon void-of-course begins 1:20 PM EDT
Moon enters Aquarius ♒ 7:22 PM EDT
Last Quarter ◑ 9:36 PM EDT

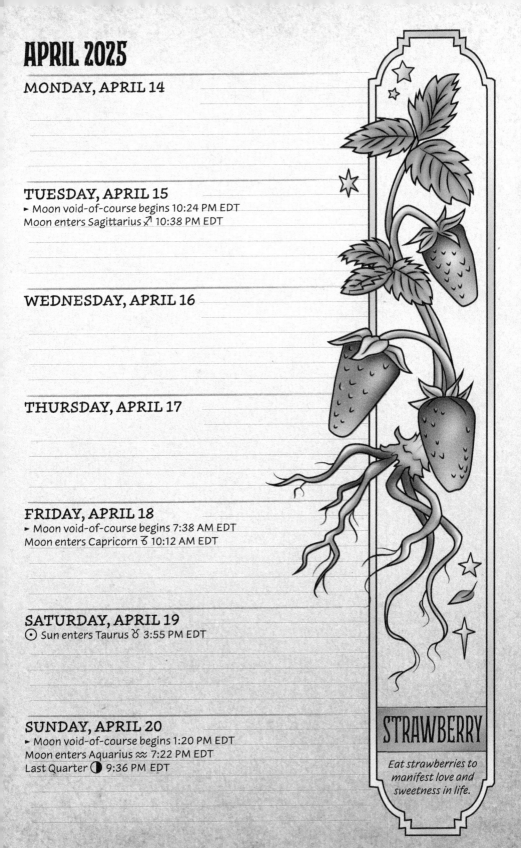

STRAWBERRY

Eat strawberries to manifest love and sweetness in life.

APRIL 2025

MONDAY, APRIL 21

TUESDAY, APRIL 22
► Moon void-of-course begins 5:55 PM EDT

WEDNESDAY, APRIL 23
Moon enters Pisces ♓ 1:06 AM EDT

Mugwort

THURSDAY, APRIL 24
► Moon void-of-course begins 10:57 PM EDT

Elderflowers

FRIDAY, APRIL 25
Moon enters Aries ♈ 3:23 AM EDT

Violets

SATURDAY, APRIL 26
► Moon void-of-course begins 12:17 PM EDT

SUNDAY, APRIL 27
Moon enters Taurus ♉ 3:16 AM EDT
New Moon ● ♉ 3:30 PM EDT

BELTANE

Feel magical energy growing with your intentions.
Cast flowers into a fire or body of water as you
make a wish for something wonderful.

APRIL/MAY 2025

MONDAY, APRIL 28

TUESDAY, APRIL 29
➤ Moon void-of-course begins 1:18 AM EDT
Moon enters Gemini ♊ 2:34 AM EDT

WEDNESDAY, APRIL 30
➤ Moon void-of-course begins 11:48 AM EDT

THURSDAY, MAY 1
★ Beltane (Fixed Festival Date)
Moon enters Cancer ♋ 3:23 AM EDT

FRIDAY, MAY 2

SATURDAY, MAY 3
➤ Moon void-of-course begins 4:01 AM EDT
Moon enters Leo ♌ 7:30 AM EDT

SUNDAY, MAY 4
First Quarter ◗ 9:52 AM EDT
℞ Pluto Retrograde begins (ends October 13)

SQUIRREL

The energy of playful cleverness.

INTUITION • REFLECTION • VISION & INTENTION
IMPORTANT THINGS • GOALS

Ground yourself with earthy incense like patchouli, cypress, or vetivert root.

THIS MONTH:

Beltane: May 1-5
Pluto Retrograde: May 4-Oct. 13
Full Moon in Scorpio: May 12
Sun enters Gemini: May 20
New Moon in Gemini: May 26

Agate will help you cultivate stability.

Cypress invokes spiritual strength.

Patchouli can assist in bringing dreams to reality.

Rosemary strengthens your aura.

Burn rosemary to receive divine guidance.

MAY

THE MAGIC OF GOAT

Goat awakens the beast within, fueling your witch's power and resolve to reach new levels. *Ask Goat how to harness your inner strength.*

Sit with the energy of Goat for 90 seconds.

What message did you receive from Goat?

COMFREY will help you heal and manifest abundance.

GARNET brings wisdom to turn desires into reality.

SPIRALS Small steps that lead to change

BLOODSTONE cultivates courage and strength to overcome challenges.

PANSIES Pensive yet down-to-earth, they strengthen the body-mind connection.

LEARNING GOAT'S MAGIC
EMPOWERING THE BEAST WITHIN

There are few animals that evoke "witch power" more than Goat! Goat embodies stability, growth, and determination to reach new heights. Find yourself in this feeling of empowerment by channeling Goat magic in a spell.

PREPARE: Prepare a mirror where you'll feel at ease chanting aloud. Light candles, burn incense, or cast ritual formalities as desired. You might like to mix up a dark, earthy anointing oil or incense blend with patchouli, cinnamon, and clove to enhance and evoke Goat power.

PERFORM THE SPELL: Look into the mirror, and gaze intently into your own eyes. Continue until you feel a sense of connection, often marked by a smile or a twinge of self-love.

Chant empowering words, perhaps something to honor Goat: *"The beast within. The Goat's* ascent. Witch's power. Strength unbent." Or the classic, *"Earth my body, water my blood, air my breath, and fire my spirit."*

When your chanting or energy peaks, hold your hands out in front of you about six inches apart. Focus on the energy between your palms, allowing it to vibrate up your arms and through your entire body. Rub your palms together if needed to feel this empowering energy.

Place your energized hands over your eyes, letting the energy flow through you. Remove your hands and look directly into the mirror.

Envision yourself with goat horns, embodying the strength, determination, and climbing prowess of Goat. Say, *"The magic is within me,"* followed by, *"And so it shall be,"* or any closing words of your choice.

MAY 2025

- Periwinkle & Herkimer Diamonds -
"Witch Power" to pursue your soul's work.

	SUNDAY	MONDAY	TUESDAY
	27 New Moon ● ♉	**28**	**29**
	4 First Quarter ◐	★Beltane 1:58 AM EDT **5**	**6**
	11	**12** Full Moon ○ ♏	**13**
	18	**19**	☉ Sun enters Gemini ♊ **20** Last Quarter ◑
	25	**26** New Moon ● ♊	**27**

INTENTIONS
Ground Yourself.

WEDNESDAY	THURSDAY	FRIDAY	SATURDAY
30	★ Beltane (Fixed Date) 1	2	3
7	8	9	10
14	15	16	17
21	22	23	24
28	29	30	31

MAY 2025

MONDAY, MAY 5
★ Beltane (Astronomical Date) 1:58 AM EDT
► Moon void-of-course begins 9:04 AM EDT
Moon enters Virgo ♍ 3:39 PM EDT

TUESDAY, MAY 6

WEDNESDAY, MAY 7

THURSDAY, MAY 8
► Moon void-of-course begins 12:11 AM EDT
Moon enters Libra ♎ 3:07 AM EDT

FRIDAY, MAY 9

SATURDAY, MAY 10
► Moon void-of-course begins 2:18 AM EDT
Moon enters Scorpio ♏ 3:59 PM EDT

SUNDAY, MAY 11

Music and sound are keys to the magical laws of the universe. Use music or sound to shift your energy.

MAY 2025

MONDAY, MAY 12
Full Moon ○ ♏ 12:56 PM EDT

TUESDAY, MAY 13
► Moon void-of-course begins 2:37 AM EDT
Moon enters Sagittarius ♐ 4:35 AM EDT

WEDNESDAY, MAY 14

THURSDAY, MAY 15
► Moon void-of-course begins 2:29 PM EDT
Moon enters Capricorn ♑ 3:58 PM EDT

FRIDAY, MAY 16

SATURDAY, MAY 17

SUNDAY, MAY 18
► Moon void-of-course begins 12:27 AM EDT
Moon enters Aquarius ♒ 1:29 AM EDT

HORNS

Fill a horn with protective herbs like sage and basil.

MAY 2025

MONDAY, MAY 19

TUESDAY, MAY 20
Last Quarter ☽ 7:59 AM EDT
► Moon void-of-course begins 7:59 AM EDT
Moon enters Pisces ♓ 8:28 AM EDT
☉ Sun enters Gemini ♊ 2:54 PM EDT

WEDNESDAY, MAY 21

THURSDAY, MAY 22
► Moon void-of-course begins 12:07 PM EDT
Moon enters Aries ♈ 12:26 PM EDT

FRIDAY, MAY 23

SATURDAY, MAY 24
► Moon void-of-course begins 7:43 AM EDT
Moon enters Taurus ♉ 1:38 PM EDT

SUNDAY, MAY 25

*Burn patchouli & bay to summon
the Greek God of the Wild, Pan.*

MAY/JUNE 2025

MONDAY, MAY 26
▶ Moon void-of-course begins 9:51 AM EDT
Moon enters Gemini ♊ 1:22 PM EDT
New Moon ● ♊ 11:03 PM EDT

TUESDAY, MAY 27

WEDNESDAY, MAY 28
▶ Moon void-of-course begins 9:00 AM EDT
Moon enters Cancer ♋ 1:32 PM EDT

THURSDAY, MAY 29

FRIDAY, MAY 30
▶ Moon void-of-course 12:51 PM EDT
Moon enters Leo ♌ 4:16 PM EDT

SATURDAY, MAY 31

SUNDAY, JUNE 1
▶ Moon void-of-course begins 7:38 PM EDT
Moon enters Virgo ♍ 11:00 PM EDT

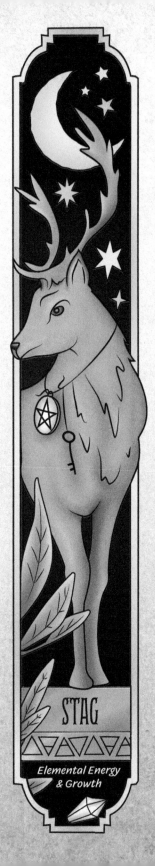

STAG

Elemental Energy & Growth

Fly Agaric (poison!) opens a portal from the mundane to the magical world.

THIS MONTH:

Full Moon in Sagittarius: June 11
Litha (Summer Solstice): June 20
Sun enters Cancer: June 20
New Moon in Cancer: June 25

Basil invokes your witch's spirit.

Honeysuckle helps you find joy in life.

Peridot shifts spiritual power to the present.

JUNE
THE MAGIC OF TOAD

Toad teaches that there's magic within you and all around you... if you're willing to look for it.

Ask Toad to reveal the magic in everyday life.

Sit with the energy of Toad for 90 seconds.

What message did you receive from Toad?

FLUORITE
clears your aura and raises magical energy.

TRANSFORMATION
Magic is real and within your grasp!

YARROW
Bathe with yarrow to enliven your body & spirit.

NEBULASTONE
can help you transform and bring your dreams to reality on Earth.

ELDER
The spirit of magic.

LEARNING TOAD'S MAGIC
TRANSFORMING THE MUNDANE TO MAGICAL

Feeling bogged down by the mundane? Want to transform yourself back into a magical creature? Toad and Frog will show you how to feel the presence of magic in everyday life.

Toad and Frog are beloved familiars. They symbolize metamorphosis and the mystical connection between earth and water—the thread that ties reality and dreams.

On a full or waxing moon, gather a bowl of water and a sprig of rosemary or mugwort to burn.

Set the bowl of water outside or near a window under the light of the moon. Burn the herbs over the water and invite the wise presence of Toad.

Scry into the water by gazing into the bowl, eyes unfocused. Waft the smoke over the bowl and say, *"Ribbit Ribbit, Croak, Croak. Refresh my magic through this smoke."*

Deeply smell the scent of the herbs and recall a time when you felt the true presence of magic. Vow to be aware of magic in everyday life—to expect it, look for it, and wait for it to be revealed.

Let the water sit under the moon overnight. Collect it before dawn and put it in a bottle or jar labeled "Toad Water." Perform this bathing spell anytime you wish to revisit Toad's magic:

Prepare a bath or shower. Pour the Toad Water into your bath or over your head or shoulders. Again, recall a time where you knew that magic was real. Find this feeling and hang onto it as you feel the sensation of water on your body.

After the spell and any time in the future—as you experience water or see Toad or Frog, you will recall this "knowing" that magic is real and ready to be revealed to you at any moment.

JUNE 2025

	SUNDAY	MONDAY	TUESDAY
	1	2 First Quarter ☽	3
	8	9	10
	15	16	17
	22	23	24
	29	30	1

- Malachite -
Evolution &
Transformation

INTENTIONS
Believe You Can Transform.

WEDNESDAY	THURSDAY	FRIDAY	SATURDAY
4	5	6	7
11 Full Moon ○ ♐	12	13	14
18 Last Quarter ◗	19	20 ★Litha (Summer Solstice) ☉ Sun enters Cancer ♋	21
25 New Moon ♋	26	27	28
2 First Quarter ◗	3	4	5

JUNE 2025

MONDAY, JUNE 2
First Quarter ◑ 11:41 PM EDT

TUESDAY, JUNE 3

WEDNESDAY, JUNE 4
► Moon void-of-course begins 7:12 AM EDT
Moon enters Libra ♎ 9:39 AM EDT

THURSDAY, JUNE 5

FRIDAY, JUNE 6
► Moon void-of-course begins 9:05 PM EDT
Moon enters Scorpio ♏ 10:23 PM EDT

SATURDAY, JUNE 7

SUNDAY, JUNE 8

SNAIL
*The spiral of a snail's shell represents the magic of
growing and transforming with slow, steady progress.*

JUNE 2025

MONDAY, JUNE 9
► Moon void-of-course begins 8:06 AM EDT
Moon enters Sagittarius ♐ 10:56 AM EDT

TUESDAY, JUNE 10

WEDNESDAY, JUNE 11
Full Moon ○ ♐ 3:44 AM EDT
► Moon void-of-course begins 3:58 PM EDT
Moon enters Capricorn ♑ 9:55 PM EDT

THURSDAY, JUNE 12

FRIDAY, JUNE 13

SATURDAY, JUNE 14
► Moon void-of-course begins 4:52 AM EDT
Moon enters Aquarius ♒ 7:00 AM EDT

SUNDAY, JUNE 15

TOADSTOOL

If you find a toadstool, make a wish and remember that magic is real.

JUNE 2025

MONDAY, JUNE 16
▸ Moon void-of-course begins 1:31 PM EDT
Moon enters Pisces ♓ 2:09 PM EDT

TUESDAY, JUNE 17

WEDNESDAY, JUNE 18
▸ Moon void-of-course begins 5:34 PM EDT
Moon enters Aries ♈ 7:08 PM EDT
Last Quarter ◐ 3:19 PM EDT

THURSDAY, JUNE 19

FRIDAY, JUNE 20
▸ Moon void-of-course begins 9:49 PM EDT
Moon enters Taurus ♉ 9:52 PM EDT
★ Litha (Summer Solstice) 10:42 PM EDT
⊙ Sun enters Cancer ♋ 10:42 PM EDT

SATURDAY, JUNE 21

SUNDAY, JUNE 22
▸ Moon void-of-course begins 9:50 PM EDT
Moon enters Gemini ♊ 10:57 PM EDT

Sweet Woodruff

LITHA

Feel the magic of the sun. Remember that you can change, grow, and live a bright life by working with herbs like cinquefoil, woodruff, and cinnamon.

JUNE 2025

MONDAY, JUNE 23
▸ Moon void-of-course begins 4:26 AM EDT

TUESDAY, JUNE 24
Moon enters Cancer ♋ 11:43 PM EDT

WEDNESDAY, JUNE 25
New Moon ● ♋ 6:31 AM EDT

THURSDAY, JUNE 26

FRIDAY, JUNE 27
▸ Moon void-of-course begins 1:15 AM EDT
Moon enters Leo ♌ 2:06 AM EDT

SATURDAY, JUNE 28

SUNDAY, JUNE 29
▸ Moon void-of-course begins 7:03 AM EDT
Moon enters Virgo ♍ 7:44 AM EDT

DRAGONFLY

The power of transformation and spiritual growth.

JUNE/JULY 2025

MONDAY, JUNE 30

TUESDAY, JULY 1
► Moon void-of-course begins 4:47 PM EDT
Moon enters Libra ♎ 5:17 PM EDT

WEDNESDAY, JULY 2
First Quarter ◑ 3:30 PM EDT
► Moon void-of-course begins 3:30 PM EDT

THURSDAY, JULY 3

FRIDAY, JULY 4
Moon enters Scorpio ♏ 5:32 AM EDT
♆℞ Neptune Retrograde begins (ends December 10)

SATURDAY, JULY 5

SUNDAY, JULY 6
► Moon void-of-course begins 6:04 PM EDT
Moon enters Sagittarius ♐ 6:06 PM EDT

*Collect rainwater or morning dew to cleanse
your magical tools and water-safe crystals.*

FUCHSITE

Use fuchsite to regain your footing and spark your inner power.

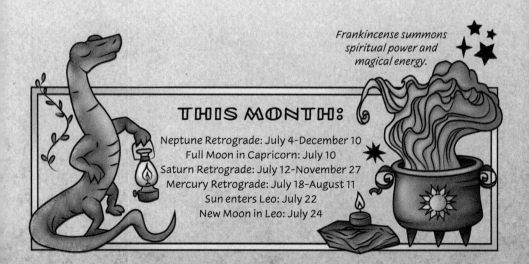

*Frankincense summons
spiritual power and
magical energy.*

THIS MONTH:

Neptune Retrograde: July 4–December 10
Full Moon in Capricorn: July 10
Saturn Retrograde: July 12–November 27
Mercury Retrograde: July 18–August 11
Sun enters Leo: July 22
New Moon in Leo: July 24

Flint sparks the energy of fire and change.

Cloves protect from unwanted energy.

The element of fire destroys to recreate.

JULY
MAGIC OF SALAMANDER
Salamander ignites the power of knowing who you are,
so you can release misconceptions about yourself.
Ask Salamander for counsel on which stories to burn.

Sit with the energy of Salamander for 90 seconds.

What message did you receive from Salamander?

THE SUN
Self-knowledge & the magic of re-inventing yourself.

AMARANTH
symbolizes the immortality of your soul.

ORANGE SELENITE
reinvigorates the fire of your soul.

OBSIDIAN
can help you realize deep truths about who you are.

CINNAMON
raises spiritual energy and enlivens your body, mind, and spirit.

LEARNING SALAMANDER'S MAGIC
THE POWER OF RE-INVENTING YOURSELF

Salamander's magic is entwined with the element of fire. Ancient lore falsely believed that salamanders were fireproof, but in truth, salamanders thrive in cool, moist environments.

Have you ever been terribly misunderstood? Misconceptions feel hurtful and they may limit your potential, especially if you begin to believe them. However, you can turn these stories into "fire" to ignite the truth of who you actually are and the expansiveness of who you wish to be.

Salamander symbolizes the mercurial spirit of the soul in alchemy, which means you can change. Releasing untruths allows you to use your power and magic for personal growth.

Write down how you've been misunderstood, and how that misunderstanding came to be.

Perform one of these spells, then write a new story about who you are, and who you intend to be.

Candle Spell: Anoint a candle with oil and roll it in fiery herbs (rosemary, salt, basil, or bay). Light the candle and focus on the power of the flame. Burn your paper and the energy of the misconceptions.

Casting Flames: Light a fire using a fire-safe bowl, cauldron, or outdoor fire pit. Cast a pinch of fiery herbs into the flames, then burn your paper of self-truths and misconceptions, releasing yourself to reclaim the "real" version of you.

Kitchen Magic: If you can't work with open flames or candles, use the secular-sacred ritual of cooking. As you cook, focus on fire's transformational power. Consume your creation, knowing it's infused with the Salamander magic: the fire of truth to create who you are.

JULY 2025

	SUNDAY	MONDAY	TUESDAY
	29	30	1
	6	7	8
	13	14	15
	20	21	22 ⊙ Sun enters Leo ♌
	27	28	29

INTENTIONS

Rewrite the stories you tell yourself.

WEDNESDAY	THURSDAY	FRIDAY	SATURDAY
2 First Quarter ◑	3	4	5
9	10 Full Moon ○ ♑	11	12
16	17 Last Quarter ◐	18	19
23	24 New Moon ● ♌	25	26
30	31	★Lughnasadh (Fixed Date) 1 First Quarter ◑	2

JULY 2025

MONDAY, JULY 7
► Moon void-of-course begins 5:30 PM EDT

TUESDAY, JULY 8

WEDNESDAY, JULY 9
Moon enters Capricorn ♑ 4:55 AM EDT

THURSDAY, JULY 10
Full Moon ○ ♑ 4:36 PM EDT
► Moon void-of-course begins 4:36 PM EDT

FRIDAY, JULY 11
Moon enters Aquarius ♒ 1:22 PM EDT

SATURDAY, JULY 12
► Moon void-of-course begins 3:45 PM EDT
♄℞ Saturn Retrograde begins (ends November 27)

SUNDAY, JULY 13
Moon enters Pisces ♓ 7:44 PM EDT

*Anoint candles or burn an oil
lamp with olive oil and a few
drops of cypress or cinnamon oil.*

JULY 2025

MONDAY, JULY 14

TUESDAY, JULY 15
► Moon void-of-course begins 1:10 PM EDT

WEDNESDAY, JULY 16
Moon enters Aries ♈ 12:32 AM EDT

THURSDAY, JULY 17
Last Quarter ◑ 8:38 PM EDT
► Moon void-of-course begins 8:38 PM EDT

FRIDAY, JULY 18
Moon enters Taurus ♉ 3:59 AM EDT
☿℞ Mercury Retrograde begins (ends August 11)

SATURDAY, JULY 19

SUNDAY, JULY 20
► Moon void-of-course begins 2:44 AM EDT
Moon enters Gemini ♊ 6:22 AM EDT

PHOENIX

Reinvent yourself whenever it's necessary.

JULY 2025

MONDAY, JULY 21
► Moon void-of-course begins 3:52 PM EDT

TUESDAY, JULY 22
Moon enters Cancer ♋ 8:27 AM EDT
☉ Sun enters Leo ♌ 9:29 AM EDT

WEDNESDAY, JULY 23
► Moon void-of-course begins 8:43 PM EDT

THURSDAY, JULY 24
Moon enters Leo ♌ 11:29 AM EDT
New Moon ● ♌ 3:11 PM EDT

FRIDAY, JULY 25

SATURDAY, JULY 26
► Moon void-of-course begins 7:02 AM EDT
Moon enters Virgo ♍ 4:56 PM EDT

SUNDAY, JULY 27

LUGHNASADH

*Feel the magic of gratitude. Harvest
berries or herbs, or bake, eat, and enjoy an
abundance of these things in a ritual meal.*

JULY/AUGUST 2025

MONDAY, JULY 28
▸ Moon void-of-course begins 8:57 PM EDT

TUESDAY, JULY 29
Moon enters Libra ♎ 1:43 AM EDT
▸ Moon void-of-course begins 11:59 PM EDT

WEDNESDAY, JULY 30

THURSDAY, JULY 31
Moon enters Scorpio ♏ 1:25 PM EDT

FRIDAY, AUGUST 1
★ Lughnasadh (Fixed Festival Date)
First Quarter ☽ 8:42 AM EDT

SATURDAY, AUGUST 2
▸ Moon void-of-course begins 9:07 PM EDT

SUNDAY, AUGUST 3
Moon enters Sagittarius ♐ 2:01 AM EDT

SUNSTONE

*Express yourself
authentically.*

*Chrysoprase connects you
to your heart's desires.*

THIS MONTH:

Lughnasadh: August 1-7
Full Moon in Aquarius: August 9
Mercury Retrograde Ends: August 11
Sun enters Virgo: August 22
New Moon in Virgo: August 23

Cast a protective magic circle with ivy.

Aromatherapy shifts your energy through scent.

Serpentine embodies Snake's power to change.

Alchemy is a process of transformation.

AUGUST
THE MAGIC OF SNAKE

Snake magic embodies healing and transformation, shedding old layers and letting go of the past.
Ask Snake how you can regenerate and renew.

Sit with the energy of Snake for 90 seconds.

What message did you receive from Snake?

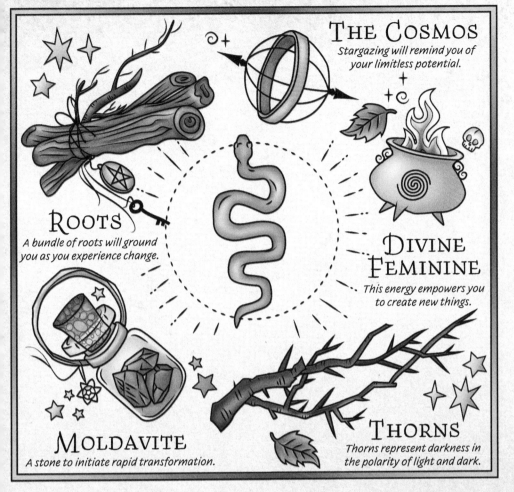

THE COSMOS
Stargazing will remind you of
your limitless potential.

ROOTS
A bundle of roots will ground
you as you experience change.

DIVINE FEMININE
This energy empowers you
to create new things.

MOLDAVITE
A stone to initiate rapid transformation.

THORNS
Thorns represent darkness in
the polarity of light and dark.

LEARNING SNAKE'S MAGIC
EMPOWERING YOURSELF TO CHANGE

Snakes are a potent and ancient symbol for healing and transmuting life's "poisons" into wisdom, growth, and change.

Snakes are known for their ability to shed their skin. They offer profound insights into the magic of letting go of the past and emerging renewed. This spell is ideal if you're feeling stuck or doubting your power to change or grow.

Use this spell to affirm your transformational abilities, no matter the circumstances.

Procure a three-foot length of ribbon or cord. Decide what you wish to change or how you wish to grow beyond self-imposed limitations.

Tie nine evenly spaced knots and envision Snake's wisdom guiding your spell as you chant. Trust Snake, as they will show you how to release the past and embrace new possibilities.

By knot of one, the spell's begun
By knot of two, the Snake renews
By knot of three, I slither free
By knot of four, unlock the door
By knot of five, I feel alive
By knot of six, this magic is quick
By knot of seven, I've learned the lesson
By knot of eight, the Serpent's fate
By knot of nine, the change is mine

Enhance your ritual by incorporating shed snake skin, either by weaving it into the knots, carrying it in a charm bag, or burning it as you prepare the knotted cord. Snake skin is a powerful spellcasting ingredient, especially if found in the wild.

Once completed, your knotted cord serves as a talisman of change.

AUGUST 2025

	SUNDAY	MONDAY	TUESDAY
	27	28	29
	3	4	5
	10	11	12
	17	18	19
	24	25	26
	31 First Quarter ◑	1	2

INTENTIONS
Lighten Your Load.

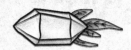

WEDNESDAY	THURSDAY	FRIDAY	SATURDAY
		★ Lughnasadh (Fixed Date)	
30	31	1 First Quarter ◑	2
	★ Lughnasadh 1:52 AM EDT		
6	7	8	9 Full Moon ○ ♒
13	14	15	16 Last Quarter ◑
		☉ Sun enters Virgo ♍	
20	21	22	23 New Moon ● ♍
27	28	29	30
3	4	5	6

AUGUST 2025

MONDAY, AUGUST 4

TUESDAY, AUGUST 5
► Moon void-of-course begins 11:29 AM EDT
Moon enters Capricorn ♑ 1:04 PM EDT

WEDNESDAY, AUGUST 6
► Moon void-of-course begins 1:39 PM EDT

THURSDAY, AUGUST 7
★ Lughnasadh (Astronomical Date) 1:52 AM EDT
Moon enters Aquarius ♒ 9:18 PM EDT

FRIDAY, AUGUST 8

SATURDAY, AUGUST 9
Full Moon ○ ♒ 3:55 AM EDT
► Moon void-of-course begins 3:55 AM EDT

SUNDAY, AUGUST 10
Moon enters Pisces ♓ 2:50 AM EDT

- Nehebkau -
The Egyptian God of
snakes & the underworld.

AUGUST 2025

MONDAY, AUGUST 11
► Moon void-of-course begins 2:55 AM EDT
☿℞ Mercury Retrograde ends

TUESDAY, AUGUST 12
Moon enters Aries ♈ 6:33 AM EDT

WEDNESDAY, AUGUST 13
► Moon void-of-course begins 6:54 PM EDT

THURSDAY, AUGUST 14
Moon enters Taurus ♉ 9:21 AM EDT

FRIDAY, AUGUST 15

SATURDAY, AUGUST 16
Last Quarter ◑ 1:12 AM EDT
► Moon void-of-course begins 1:12 AM EDT
Moon enters Gemini ♊ 12:01 PM EDT

SUNDAY, AUGUST 17

BURDOCK

Drink burdock root tea to release bitterness of the past.

AUGUST 2025

MONDAY, AUGUST 18
► Moon void-of-course begins 7:53 AM EDT
Moon enters Cancer ♋ 3:05 PM EDT

TUESDAY, AUGUST 19

WEDNESDAY, AUGUST 20
► Moon void-of-course begins 8:27 AM EDT
Moon enters Leo ♌ 7:17 PM EDT

THURSDAY, AUGUST 21
► Moon void-of-course begins 2:14 PM EDT

FRIDAY, AUGUST 22
☉ Sun enters Virgo ♍ 4:33 PM EDT

SATURDAY, AUGUST 23
Moon enters Virgo ♍ 1:24 AM EDT
New Moon ● ♍ 2:07 AM EDT

SUNDAY, AUGUST 24

- Ouroboros -
The eternal cycle of life, death, and rebirth.

AUGUST 2025

MONDAY, AUGUST 25
▸ Moon void-of-course begins 9:54 AM EDT
Moon enters Libra ♎ 10:07 AM EDT

TUESDAY, AUGUST 26
▸ Moon void-of-course begins 10:07 PM EDT

WEDNESDAY, AUGUST 27
Moon enters Scorpio ♏ 9:28 PM EDT

THURSDAY, AUGUST 28

FRIDAY, AUGUST 29
▸ Moon void-of-course begins 8:47 PM EDT

SATURDAY, AUGUST 30
Moon enters Sagittarius ♐ 10:04 AM EDT

SUNDAY, AUGUST 31
First Quarter ◑ 2:25 AM EDT

DRAGON

Use the symbol of Dragon to banish unwanted energy.

The symbol of henbane (poison) helps you to fly beyond your limitations.

THIS MONTH:

Uranus Retrograde: September 6-Feb. 3, 2026
Full Moon in Pisces: September 7
Lunar Eclipse: September 7
Partial Solar Eclipse: September 21
New Moon in Virgo: September 21
Mabon (Equinox): September 22
Sun enters Libra: September 22

Onyx unlocks your inner guidance.

Agrimony releases heavy energy.

SEPTEMBER
THE MAGIC OF RAVEN
Raven unlocks the magic of lighthearted flight,
teaching you the power of play.
Ask Raven how to be playful in magic and life.

Sit with the energy of Raven for 90 seconds.

What message did you receive from Raven?

DARK MOON
Your unlimited potential.

TURQUOISE
Dissolving self-sabotage.

WITCH HAZEL
The power to see a magical new future.

TOURMALINE
Clears doubts and fears so you can trust yourself to fly.

IRIS
A symbol of hope and better things to come.

LEARNING RAVEN'S MAGIC
THE FREEDOM TO TAKE FLIGHT

Caw! Caw! Raven and Crow speak of the laws of the universe, and they'll tell you their secrets... if you ask. *Spoiler alert: when you are heavy, you cannot fly.* Sometimes we take life and magic too seriously, and Raven will show you how to lighten your mood so you can truly take flight.

PREPARE: Perform this spell at night or dawn before the sun rises. Create a sacred space with woodsy incense like benzoin or cypress. If Raven has gifted you a feather, it's a sacred object for your spellwork. Wear it in your witch's hat, set it on your altar, or hold it during this spell.

If you aren't into "journey" spells, go on a Raven quest! Venture out and find a flock of ravens in real life. Observe them until you pick up some clues about how you can be more light, playful, and clever as you act to manifest your intentions.

PERFORM THE VISION SPELL: Close your eyes and imagine yourself transforming into a raven.

Take flight into the dark sky, feeling the cool air against your feathers. Fly over your neighborhood, then decide where you want to go—what future do you desire?

As you fly higher, view the landscape below. It'll show you a map filled with symbols and clues. Let Raven's perspective reveal how to use your magic creatively and see life as a game. How can you make things a little more fun? How can you have faith in yourself and work with the laws of natural magic in a lighter, more playful way?

Once you've received some clues, envision the route back to where you began. Ground yourself, and make sure to write notes about what Raven showed you on your journey.

SEPTEMBER 2025

Summon the Goddess Morrigan and her ravens with an incense blend of mugwort, rosemary, sage, patchouli, and marigold.

	SUNDAY	MONDAY	TUESDAY
	31 First Quarter ◑	**1**	**2**
	Lunar Eclipse **7** Full Moon ○ ♓	**8**	**9**
	14 Last Quarter ◐	**15**	**16**
	Partial Solar Eclipse **21** New Moon ● ♍	☉ Sun enters Libra ♎ ★ Mabon (Autumnal Equinox) **22**	**23**
	28	**29** First Quarter ◑	**30**

INTENTIONS
Embody a playful energy.

WEDNESDAY	THURSDAY	FRIDAY	SATURDAY
3	4	5	6
10	11	12	13
17	18	19	20
24	25	26	27
1	2	3	4

SEPTEMBER 2025

MONDAY, SEPTEMBER 1
➤ Moon void-of-course begins 9:39 PM EDT
Moon enters Capricorn ♑ 9:45 PM EDT

TUESDAY, SEPTEMBER 2

WEDNESDAY, SEPTEMBER 3

THURSDAY, SEPTEMBER 4
➤ Moon void-of-course begins 6:08 AM EDT
Moon enters Aquarius ♒ 6:32 AM EDT

FRIDAY, SEPTEMBER 5
➤ Moon void-of-course begins 4:52 PM EDT

SATURDAY, SEPTEMBER 6
Moon enters Pisces ♓ 11:55 AM EDT
♅℞ Uranus Retrograde begins (ends Feb. 3, 2026)

SUNDAY, SEPTEMBER 7
Full Moon ○ ♓ 2:09 PM EDT
Lunar Eclipse 2:12 PM EDT

Arrange a raven's skull, a feather, and a knife on your altar to summon spiritual clarity to make wise decisions.

SEPTEMBER 2025

MONDAY, SEPTEMBER 8
▸ Moon void-of-course begins 1:44 PM EDT
Moon enters Aries ♈ 2:36 PM EDT

TUESDAY, SEPTEMBER 9

WEDNESDAY, SEPTEMBER 10
▸ Moon void-of-course begins 2:54 AM EDT
Moon enters Taurus ♉ 4:03 PM EDT

THURSDAY, SEPTEMBER 11

FRIDAY, SEPTEMBER 12
▸ Moon void-of-course begins 4:13 PM EDT
Moon enters Gemini ♊ 5:39 PM EDT

SATURDAY, SEPTEMBER 13

SUNDAY, SEPTEMBER 14
Last Quarter ◑ 6:33 AM EDT
▸ Moon void-of-course begins 6:47 PM EDT
Moon enters Cancer ♋ 8:30 PM EDT

UMBRELLA

Tuck a rose in your umbrella or hat to heighten your intuition.

SEPTEMBER 2025

MONDAY, SEPTEMBER 15

TUESDAY, SEPTEMBER 16
► Moon void-of-course begins 11:14 PM EDT

WEDNESDAY, SEPTEMBER 17
Moon enters Leo ♌ 1:20 AM EDT

THURSDAY, SEPTEMBER 18

FRIDAY, SEPTEMBER 19
► Moon void-of-course begins 8:22 AM EDT
Moon enters Virgo ♍ 8:23 AM EDT

SATURDAY, SEPTEMBER 20

SUNDAY, SEPTEMBER 21
Partial Solar Eclipse 3:42 PM EDT
New Moon ● ♍ 3:54 PM EDT
► Moon void-of-course begins 3:54 PM EDT
Moon enters Libra ♎ 5:41 PM EDT

MABON

*Feel the magic of release. Courageously follow
your intuition towards what you desire, and
allow yourself to slowly let go of the rest.*

SEPTEMBER 2025

MONDAY, SEPTEMBER 22
☉ Sun enters Libra ♎ 2:19 PM EDT
★ Mabon (Autumnal Equinox) 2:19 PM EDT

TUESDAY, SEPTEMBER 23
► Moon void-of-course begins 12:02 PM EDT

WEDNESDAY, SEPTEMBER 24
Moon enters Scorpio ♏ 5:00 AM EDT

THURSDAY, SEPTEMBER 25

FRIDAY, SEPTEMBER 26
► Moon void-of-course begins 1:44 PM EDT
Moon enters Sagittarius ♐ 5:37 PM EDT

SATURDAY, SEPTEMBER 27

SUNDAY, SEPTEMBER 28

VULTURE

Carry a vulture's feather to help you accept change.

SEPTEMBER/OCTOBER 2025

MONDAY, SEPTEMBER 29
First Quarter ◑ 7:54 PM EDT
► Moon void-of-course begins 1:44 AM EDT
Moon enters Capricorn ♑ 5:55 AM EDT

TUESDAY, SEPTEMBER 30

WEDNESDAY, OCTOBER 1
► Moon void-of-course begins 11:34 AM EDT
Moon enters Aquarius ♒ 3:52 PM EDT

THURSDAY, OCTOBER 2

FRIDAY, OCTOBER 3
► Moon void-of-course begins 2:15 PM EDT
Moon enters Pisces ♓ 10:06 PM EDT

SATURDAY, OCTOBER 4

SUNDAY, OCTOBER 5
► Moon void-of-course begins 8:30 PM EDT

*Create a simple ritual that makes
you feel powerful and alive.*

BEAR

Channel Bear's spirit to summon courage and strength.

INTUITION • REFLECTION • VISION & INTENTION
IMPORTANT THINGS • GOALS

Light a black candle at midnight to align with the magic of the night.

THIS MONTH:

Full Moon in Aries: October 6
Pluto Retrograde Ends: Oct. 13
New Moon in Libra: October 21
Sun enters Scorpio: October 22
Samhain: Oct. 31– Nov. 6

Sandalwood will calm you in the darkness.

Use a blackthorn wand to help you make difficult changes.

Look through a hagstone and make a wish.

OCTOBER
THE MAGIC OF BAT
Bat will give you courage as you fly through darkness and into the unknown.
Ask Bat how you can let go and soar.

Sit with the energy of Bat for 90 seconds.

What message did you receive from Bat?

THE DARK
represents the magic of starting over and accepting change.

HAZEL
Use a hazel wand to direct energy to what you desire.

HEMATITE
A dark stone that reflects light. Gaze into it for wisdom and shadow work.

JET
can help you start over and begin again in a new direction.

MULLEIN
Cast mullein into your ritual fire to help you find light in the darkness.

LEARNING BAT'S MAGIC
FLYING THROUGH DARKNESS

Bats represent the concept of shamanic death or spiritual death—breaking down the old versions of yourself so you can begin again. However, change is hard. Yet Bat's fearless movement through the night can help make necessary change happen as easily as possible.

Spending a little time in pitch darkness can help you to realize the power of beginning again and will connect you to the energy of Bat magic.

THINGS YOU'LL NEED: A dark space to sit in silence. You might like to take a little trip to a dark place outdoors—if you're brave, safe, and able—go to the forest, to a cave, or a dark part of your yard. Or perhaps sit in a closet, a dark room, or an attic. Prepare three candles to represent past, present, and future.

CAST THE SPELL: Travel to your dark place. Light the three candles. As you light them, take a moment to feel how the concepts of "past, present, and future" feel in your body. Then one by one, blow out each candle and release the feelings associated with each place in time.

Once all of the candles have been extinguished, allow yourself a moment to sit in pitch darkness.

Then ask yourself, what no longer fits your life? What can you let go of? Decide.

Say or feel, *"With wings of Bat, though fears ignite, I trust this change and soar in flight."*

Take a moment to feel the pain or fear of letting go. Often the reluctance to feel those initial feelings is part of why it's so hard. Repeat the above phrase until your emotions shift.

Then say, *"And so it shall be. The magic of Bat will set me free."*

OCTOBER 2025

Pomegranate is a symbol of the darkness of the underworld and a reminder that light eventually returns.

	SUNDAY	MONDAY	TUESDAY
	28	29 First Quarter ◑	30
	5	6 Full Moon ○ ♈	7
	12	13 Last Quarter ◐	14
	19	20	21 New Moon ● ♎
	26	27	28

INTENTIONS
Embrace the Unknown.

WEDNESDAY	THURSDAY	FRIDAY	SATURDAY
1	2	3	4
8	9	10	11
15	16	17	18
22 ⊙ Sun enters Scorpio	23	24	25
29 First Quarter ☽	30	31 ★Samhain (fixed date)	1

OCTOBER 2025

MONDAY, OCTOBER 6
Moon enters Aries ♈ 12:48 AM EDT
Full Moon ○ ♈ 11:48 PM EDT

TUESDAY, OCTOBER 7
► Moon void-of-course begins 2:24 PM EDT

WEDNESDAY, OCTOBER 8
Moon enters Taurus ♉ 1:13 AM EDT

THURSDAY, OCTOBER 9
► Moon void-of-course begins 8:31 PM EDT

FRIDAY, OCTOBER 10
Moon enters Gemini ♊ 1:11 AM EDT

SATURDAY, OCTOBER 11
► Moon void-of-course begins 10:56 PM EDT

SUNDAY, OCTOBER 12
Moon enters Cancer ♋ 2:37 AM EDT

- Black Witch Moth -
Messages from the Other Side

OCTOBER 2025

MONDAY, OCTOBER 13
Last Quarter ◑ 2:12 PM EST
♇℞ Pluto Retrograde ends

TUESDAY, OCTOBER 14
► Moon void-of-course begins 1:05 AM EDT
Moon enters Leo ♌ 6:47 AM EDT

WEDNESDAY, OCTOBER 15

THURSDAY, OCTOBER 16
► Moon void-of-course begins 1:06 AM EDT
Moon enters Virgo ♍ 2:06 PM EDT

FRIDAY, OCTOBER 17

SATURDAY, OCTOBER 18
► Moon void-of-course begins 5:11 PM EDT

SUNDAY, OCTOBER 19
Moon enters Libra ♎ 12:01 AM EDT

OPOSSUM

Channel Opossum to embrace resilience in dark times.

OCTOBER 2025

MONDAY, OCTOBER 20

TUESDAY, OCTOBER 21
New Moon ● ♎ 8:25 AM EDT
► Moon void-of-course begins 8:25 AM EDT
Moon enters Scorpio ♏ 11:42 AM EDT

WEDNESDAY, OCTOBER 22
☉ Sun enters Scorpio ♏ 11:50 PM EDT

THURSDAY, OCTOBER 23

Scary faces on Jack-o-Lanterns will protect you!

FRIDAY, OCTOBER 24
► Moon void-of-course begins 12:14AM EDT
Moon enters Sagittarius ♐ 12:19 AM EDT

SATURDAY, OCTOBER 25

SUNDAY, OCTOBER 26
► Moon void-of-course begins 12:42 PM EDT
Moon enters Capricorn ♑ 12:54 PM EDT

SAMHAIN

*Feel the possibilities and magic in the darkness.
Create a charm bag with iron, salt, and silver to
protect your spirit as you venture into the unknown.*

OCTOBER/NOVEMBER 2025

MONDAY, OCTOBER 27

TUESDAY, OCTOBER 28
► Moon void-of-course begins 11:38 PM EDT
Moon enters Aquarius ≈ 11:56 PM EDT

WEDNESDAY, OCTOBER 29
First Quarter ◑ 12:21 PM EDT

THURSDAY, OCTOBER 30

FRIDAY, OCTOBER 31
★ Samhain (Fixed Festival Date)
► Moon void-of-course begins 2:15 AM EDT
Moon enters Pisces ⟓ 7:46 AM EDT

SATURDAY, NOVEMBER 1

SUNDAY, NOVEMBER 2
► Moon void-of-course begins 10:16 AM EST
Moon enters Aries ♈ 10:39 AM EST

SPIDER

*Channel Spider to
recreate your life.*

*Use selenite to nurture yourself
and act in your highest good.*

THIS MONTH:

Samhain: October 31-November 6
Full Moon in Taurus: November 5
Mercury Retrograde: Nov. 9-29
Jupiter ℞: Nov. 11-March 10, 2026
New Moon in Scorpio: November 20
Sun Enters Sagittarius: November 21
Saturn Retrograde Ends: November 27

Lupines symbolize living life to the fullest.

Howling at the moon frees your soul.

Moonstone will connect you to your intuition.

NOVEMBER
THE MAGIC OF WOLF
Wolf connects you to the sacred rhythms of life
and helps you to know yourself better.
Ask Wolf how you can live authentically.

Sit with the energy of Wolf for 90 seconds.

What message did you receive from Wolf?

MOON PHASES
help you remember that the energy of life waxes and wanes.

SILVER
will connect you to your intuitive powers.

ACONITE
is a symbol of breaking through boundaries.

KYANITE
clears unwanted vibrations and raises energy in ritual.

WILLOW
symbolizes the resilience and vitality of spirit.

LEARNING WOLF'S MAGIC
THE RITUAL OF KNOWING YOURSELF

Wolf magic lies in ritual and the wildness of spirit. These elements may seem contradictory, but they often go hand in hand. Rituals do not limit us—they define us.

A "ritual" doesn't have to be complicated or esoteric. Rituals are powerful even when they are simple—like noticing the seasons, sun, and moon, or caring for your "wolf-like" needs of food, shelter, and community.

Reflecting on the patterns of the sun and moon in a ritualistic manner will help you track, follow, and listen to your own wild spirit.

In the morning, think about what you can do to live authentically.

At noon, check in with your body, mind, emotions, and spirit. How can you realign?

In the evening, reflect on your day. Were you true to yourself? No judgment, just notice!

For new moons, set an intention to listen and commit to your wild spirit. What rituals, actions, or intentions will help you stay true to this?

For the waxing moon, cultivate your intuition. Listen deeply to your inner wisdom: what makes you feel good and right?

On the full moon, use the "light" and clarity to gather insights. How do you want to direct your energy? How can you feel complete and full?

During the waning moon, reflect, draw inwards, journal, meditate, and ask questions about who you are, how you can listen to yourself, and how you can release or lighten your load.

Take notes on these phases, then look back to explore coincidences, patterns, intuition, and clues on how to keep your spirit wild and free.

NOVEMBER 2025

	SUNDAY	MONDAY	TUESDAY
	26	27	28
	2	3	4
	9	10	11
	16	17	18
	23	24	25
	30	1	2

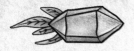

Intentions
Feel the Wild of Your Spirit

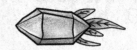

Wednesday	Thursday	Friday	Saturday
		★ Samhain (Fixed Date)	
29 First Quarter ◐	**30**	**31**	**1**
	★ Samhain 11:04 PM EST		
5 Full Moon ○ ♉	**6**	**7**	**8**
12 Last Quarter ◑	**13**	**14**	**15**
		☉ Sun Enters Sagittarius	
19	**20** New Moon ● ♏	**21**	**22**
26	**27**	**28** First Quarter ◐	**29**
3	**4** Full Moon ○ ♊	**5**	**6**

NOVEMBER 2025

MONDAY, NOVEMBER 3

TUESDAY, NOVEMBER 4
► Moon void-of-course begins 6:22 AM EST
Moon enters Taurus ♉ 11:16 AM EST

WEDNESDAY, NOVEMBER 5
Full Moon ○ ♉ 8:20 AM EST

THURSDAY, NOVEMBER 6
► Moon void-of-course begins 9:50 AM EST
Moon enters Gemini ♊ 10:20 AM EST
★ Samhain (Astronomical Date) 11:04 PM EST

FRIDAY, NOVEMBER 7

SATURDAY, NOVEMBER 8
► Moon void-of-course begins 9:31 AM EST
Moon enters Cancer ♋ 10:06 AM EST

SUNDAY, NOVEMBER 9
☿℞ Mercury Retrograde begins (ends November 29)

*Light a white candle under the full moon and
howl to connect to the wild spirit of Wolf.*

NOVEMBER 2025

MONDAY, NOVEMBER 10
▶ Moon void-of-course begins 12:23 PM EST
Moon enters Leo ♌ 12:34 PM EST

TUESDAY, NOVEMBER 11
♃ Ŗ Jupiter Retrograde begins (ends March 10, 2026)

WEDNESDAY, NOVEMBER 12
Last Quarter ◑ 12:28 AM EST
▶ Moon void-of-course begins 6:29 PM EST
Moon enters Virgo ♍ 6:52 PM EST

THURSDAY, NOVEMBER 13

FRIDAY, NOVEMBER 14

SATURDAY, NOVEMBER 15
▶ Moon void-of-course begins 4:09 AM EST
Moon enters Libra ♎ 4:44 AM EST

SUNDAY, NOVEMBER 16

FOX

*Channel Fox energy
to summon cunning
and grace.*

NOVEMBER 2025

MONDAY, NOVEMBER 17
► Moon void-of-course begins 6:51 AM EST
Moon enters Scorpio ♏ 4:45 PM EST

TUESDAY, NOVEMBER 18

WEDNESDAY, NOVEMBER 19

THURSDAY, NOVEMBER 20
New Moon ● ♏ 1:48 AM EST
► Moon void-of-course begins 4:25 AM EST
Moon enters Sagittarius ♐ 5:26 AM EST

FRIDAY, NOVEMBER 21
☉ Sun enters Sagittarius ♐ 8:35 PM EST

SATURDAY, NOVEMBER 22
► Moon void-of-course begins 4:48 PM EST
Moon enters Capricorn ♑ 5:53 PM EST

SUNDAY, NOVEMBER 23

*Wolves are pathfinders. Explore a new
direction that is calling to you.*

NOVEMBER 2025

MONDAY, NOVEMBER 24

TUESDAY, NOVEMBER 25
► Moon void-of-course begins 4:10 AM EST
Moon enters Aquarius ♒ 5:16 AM EST

WEDNESDAY, NOVEMBER 26

THURSDAY, NOVEMBER 27
► Moon void-of-course begins 12:53 PM EST
Moon enters Pisces ♓ 2:24 PM EST
♄℞ Saturn Retrograde ends

FRIDAY, NOVEMBER 28
First Quarter ◑ 1:59 AM EST

SATURDAY, NOVEMBER 29
► Moon void-of-course begins 7:05 PM EST
Moon enters Aries ♈ 8:06 PM EST
☿℞ Mercury Retrograde ends

SUNDAY, NOVEMBER 30

HOWLING

*Reconnect to
your instincts by
expressing your
voice.*

INTUITION • REFLECTION • VISION & INTENTION
IMPORTANT THINGS • GOALS

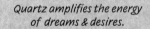

*Quartz amplifies the energy
of dreams & desires.*

THIS MONTH:

Full Moon in Gemini: December 4
Neptune Retrograde Ends: December 10
New Moon in Sagittarius: December 19
Yule (Winter Solstice): December 21
Sun enters Capricorn: December 21

Sniff a flower to remind you of magic.

Rainbows reveal magic hidden in plain sight.

DECEMBER
THE MAGIC OF UNICORN
Unicorn evokes a sense of knowing
in the possibility and power of your magic.
Ask Unicorn how to know your inner power.

What message did you receive from Unicorn?

Sit with the energy of Unicorn for 90 seconds.

SUN & MOON symbolize the law of polarity and the phases of life.

AMETHYST connects you to your divine nature.

LAVENDER will refresh your belief in love and magic.

SEASONS strengthens faith that spring will come again.

ROSE The many petals of a rose evoke infinite possibilities.

LEARNING UNICORN'S MAGIC
THE POWER OF KNOWING THAT MAGIC IS REAL

The power of Unicorn is to know that possibility, wonder, and magic exist for you, and are always at your fingertips. Your inner power (Unicorn power!) is all you need to make magic happen, and it's already within you.

PREPARE an optional sacred space. The only requirement is your own self and body, existing right now as you are. If you want to embellish: light candles, burn incense like rose, lavender, or vanilla, or drink fruit or peppermint tea. You can also hold a crystal like quartz, charoite, or garnet to help you feel your magic.

CAST YOUR SPELL. With your hand over your heart, claim what you desire or who you wish to be. Make your wish*. Decide that you can have it, and that it is possible, even if there are many steps (or obstacles) before you get there.

When you make your wish, you'll feel a spark of energy, a glimmer inside of you. That is the spark of magic and the power of Unicorn. Feel that internally, even if for a split-second, and you will spark the cauldron of magic that is within you and available to you anytime, anywhere, and in any circumstance.

Once you feel that spark, sit with it for a moment. Feel it flowing to you and through you, from the ground up through your body and out of the top of your head like a Unicorn's horn.

Repeat this spell anytime you feel lost or disconnected from your magic and intentions.

Even unicorns can't wish people back from the dead or make someone specific fall in love. Your wish must comply with the laws of physics, biology, and free will.

DECEMBER 2025

*Opal evokes the power of possibility
and the energy of divine guidance.*

	SUNDAY	MONDAY	TUESDAY
	30	1	2
	7	8	9
	14	15	16
	21 ★Yule (Winter Solstice) ☉ Sun Enters Capricorn	22	23
	28	29	30

INTENTIONS
Expect Good Things to Come.

WEDNESDAY	THURSDAY	FRIDAY	SATURDAY
3	4 Full Moon ○ ♊	5	6
10	11 Last Quarter ◑	12	13
17	18	19 New Moon ● ♐	20
24	25	26	27 First Quarter ◑
31	1	2	3 Full Moon ○ ♋

DECEMBER 2025

MONDAY, DECEMBER 1
▶ Moon void-of-course begins 1:15 PM EST
Moon enters Taurus ♉ 10:12 PM EST

TUESDAY, DECEMBER 2

WEDNESDAY, DECEMBER 3
▶ Moon void-of-course begins 8:51 PM EST
Moon enters Gemini ♊ 9:47 PM EST

THURSDAY, DECEMBER 4
Full Moon ○ ♊ 6:13 PM EST

FRIDAY, DECEMBER 5
▶ Moon void-of-course begins 7:55 PM EST
Moon enters Cancer ♋ 8:55 PM EST

SATURDAY, DECEMBER 6

SUNDAY, DECEMBER 7
▶ Moon void-of-course begins 8:44 PM EST
Moon enters Leo ♌ 9:48 PM EST

*Create a Coat of Arms with the
animal that you relate to most.*

DECEMBER 2025

MONDAY, DECEMBER 8

TUESDAY, DECEMBER 9
▶ Moon void-of-course begins 11:57 PM EST

WEDNESDAY, DECEMBER 10
Moon enters Virgo ♍ 2:20 AM EST
♆℞ Neptune Retrograde ends

THURSDAY, DECEMBER 11
Last Quarter ◑ 3:52 PM EST

FRIDAY, DECEMBER 12
▶ Moon void-of-course begins 9:51 AM EST
Moon enters Libra ♎ 11:04 AM EST

SATURDAY, DECEMBER 13

SUNDAY, DECEMBER 14
▶ Moon void-of-course begins 10:36 PM EST
Moon enters Scorpio ♏ 10:51 PM EST

POSSIBILITY

What if everything worked out better than expected?

DECEMBER 2025

MONDAY, DECEMBER 15

TUESDAY, DECEMBER 16

WEDNESDAY, DECEMBER 17
► Moon void-of-course begins 10:24 AM EST
Moon enters Sagittarius ♐ 11:39 AM EST

THURSDAY, DECEMBER 18

FRIDAY, DECEMBER 19
New Moon ● ♐ 8:44 PM EST
► Moon void-of-course begins 10:40 PM EST
Moon enters Capricorn ♑ 11:53 PM EST

SATURDAY, DECEMBER 20

SUNDAY, DECEMBER 21
★ Yule (Winter Solstice) 10:02 AM EST
☉ Sun enters Capricorn ♑ 10:02 AM EST

YULE

*Feel the magic of peace and acceptance. Decorate
your home with herbs and evergreens to bring light
and energy to yourself in the present.*

DECEMBER 2025

MONDAY, DECEMBER 22
▸ Moon void-of-course begins 9:44 AM EST
Moon enters Aquarius ♒ 10:52 AM EST

TUESDAY, DECEMBER 23

WEDNESDAY, DECEMBER 24
▸ Moon void-of-course begins 4:42 PM EST
Moon enters Pisces ♓ 8:08 PM EST

THURSDAY, DECEMBER 25

FRIDAY, DECEMBER 26

*Ivy and evergreens
symbolize the
immortality of the soul.*

SATURDAY, DECEMBER 27
▸ Moon void-of-course begins 2:04 AM EST
Moon enters Aries ♈ 3:01 AM EST
First Quarter ◗ 2:10 PM EST

SUNDAY, DECEMBER 28
▸ Moon void-of-course begins 9:13 PM EST

DECEMBER 2025/JANUARY 2026

MONDAY, DECEMBER 29
Moon enters Taurus ♉ 6:58 AM EST

TUESDAY, DECEMBER 30

WEDNESDAY, DECEMBER 31
► Moon void-of-course begins 7:24 AM EST
Moon enters Gemini ♊ 8:13 AM EST

THURSDAY, JANUARY 1, 2026

FRIDAY, JANUARY 2, 2026
► Moon void-of-course begins 7:23 AM EST
Moon enters Cancer ♋ 8:09 AM EST

SATURDAY, JANUARY 3, 2026
Full Moon ○ ♋ 5:02 AM EST

SUNDAY, JANUARY 4, 2026
► Moon void-of-course begins 8:00 AM EST
Moon enters Leo ♌ 8:43 AM EST

*Burn your Yule greens to ward off hobgoblins
(and to "clear the air" for a fresh new year!)*

Your Year of Animal Magic

GRATITUDE
Which animal are you
most grateful for?

WISDOM
Which animal taught
you something new?

RELEASE
Which animal
helped you to let go?

SUCCESS
Which animal helped
you succeed?

MAGIC
Which animal showed
you that magic is real?

SELF
Which animal helped
you to know yourself?

Keep Watching and Listening!

THERE'S ALWAYS MORE TO LEARN FROM ANIMALS.

How will you use the magic of animals?
What's next for you?!

Jessica Elliott
Color Assistant

Bollank
Color & Art Assistant

Fiona Horne
Editor of Magick
& Editor
FionaHorne.com

Wendy Ledger
Editor
WendyLedgerAuthor.com

Cora Springs Moon
Editor

THANK YOU!

About the Artist

Amy Cesari

*and her familiars
Mr. Toad & Merlin*

Amy is an author and illustrator who loves animated musicals. She also likes watercolor painting, witchcraft, and walking on the beach in a really big sun hat.

Not only does she own every Nintendo game console ever made, she's earned several fancy diplomas and enjoys continued studies in various magical practices.

CONTACT AMY AND SEE MORE BOOKS, PRINTABLE PAGES, AND ART :

Amy@ColoringBookofShadows.com
ColoringBookofShadows.com

Printed in Great Britain
by Amazon

54873326R00096